S0-BFE-121

DARWIN, MARX, and WAGNER

DARWIN MARX and WAGNER

A SYMPOSIUM

Edited by Henry L. Plaine

OHIO STATE UNIVERSITY PRESS

Library of Congress Catalogue Card Number: 61-12066

Foreword

FOLLOWING the success of the 1958 Mediaeval Conference, a group of faculty members at Ohio State planned another conference for October, 1959, dealing with the influence of three men—Charles Darwin, Karl Marx, and Richard Wagner. This combination was suggested, of course, by Jacques Barzun's well-known book *Darwin, Marx, Wagner*. Since the chief works of these three men appeared in 1859, the conference became, in effect, a centennial anniversary concerned with an appraisal of the impact of these men on both their own disciplines and upon society.

In general, the influence of each of these men on society has been both good and bad, yet undeniably significant; in one way or another, all three are symbols of radical changes in our time. Their writings are associated with the relationship between science and society, economics and society, and art and society. They have inspired brutality and cynicism, dedication and self-sacrifice, unbounded enthusiasm and bitter hatred. They represent challenges to religious beliefs and ethical values, to art, and to scholarship. Appearing against a background of growing political unrest, astounding scientific and technological advances, and an unparalleled economic expansion, the doctrines of Darwin, Marx, and Wagner were instrumental in touching off the revolutionary changes which followed.

Darwin's theory of organic evolution, with its associated

concepts of the struggle for existence and survival of the
fittest, seemed to strike at such basic concerns as religion,
philosophy, science, and politics. These and other concepts,
set forth in *Origin of Species,* accelerated the "warfare of
science with theology" and seemed to justify the individual
and group struggles of people in all walks of life. "Nature
red in tooth and claw" was used to explain why Europeans
in the latter part of the nineteenth century and the early part
of the twentieth strove to outproduce, outsell, and outcolonize
each other. The assumed superiority of certain races and people was based, falsely, on Darwinism.

Marxism was an attack on certain fundamental beliefs in
Western civilization. In a way it fulfilled the requirements of
a religion. Karl Marx's *Critique of Political Economy* is not
merely a study of economic theory, but a philosophy of history, a sociological critique, and a program for political action. Although Marx's writings were aimed at the working
class of industrialized nations, Marxism has had its greatest
impact on backward, rural countries. Nevertheless, the challenge of Marxist socialism or communism is all too evident
in our present world.

Richard Wagner developed a new art form, the music
drama. His *Tristan and Isolde* differed sharply from previous
operas of the nineteenth century, especially in its use of the
"unending" musical score, continuous dramatic action, and
the recurring musical symbol or leitmotiv. His harmonic
style and individual manner of orchestration have had a profound influence upon later composers, so that the music of
the nineteenth century has sometimes been characterized as
"before and after *Tristan.*" Quite aside from Wagner's impact on music, the cult of Wagnerism undoubtedly influenced
the growth of frenzied nationalism and prepared the way for
totalitarian dictatorships.

Andreas Dorpalen, professor of history at Ohio State University, sketches the main intellectual patterns of the last century in "Man and His Destiny: The Darwin-Marx-Wagner Debate, 1859–1959." Dr. Dorpalen has been a Guggenheim Fellow and a visiting member of the Institute for Advanced Study at Princeton and is the author of numerous articles in various scholarly journals.

Bentley Glass, professor of biology at Johns Hopkins University, and Richard Hofstadter, professor of history at Columbia University, discuss the biological and social aspects of Darwinism. Dr. Glass, a member of the National Academy of Sciences, past president of the American Association of University Professors, and the author of numerous articles on science and education, considers "Darwinism in Modern Biology." Dr. Hofstadter, who contributes "Darwinism and Western Thought," is the recipient of several awards and honors, including the Pulitzer Prize in History for 1956.

Chauncey D. Leake discusses "A Century of Confusion." Professor of pharmacology at Ohio State University, Dr. Leake is assistant dean of the College of Medicine and past president of the American Association for the Advancement of Science.

"A Century of Marx and Marxism" is contributed by Bertram D. Wolfe, historian and political scientist, and "Marxism behind the Iron Curtain" by Leonard B. Schapiro, reader in Russian government and politics in the School of Economics and Political Science at the University of London. Mr. Wolfe, who has traveled extensively in Russia and has been personally acquainted with several Soviet leaders, is an outspoken critic of totalitarianism, particularly of Soviet communism. When the Korean War started, he organized for the State Department the Ideological Advisory Staff of the Voice of America. Mr. Schapiro is the author of *The Origin*

of the Communist Autocracy and *The Communist Party of the
Soviet Union.*

The subject of Wagnerism is discussed by Joseph Kerman,
associate professor of music at the University of California,
whose subject is "Debts Paid and Debts Neglected." Dr. Kerman's historical and critical essays and reviews have appeared in leading musicological journals, and he is the author
of *Opera as Drama.*

HENRY L. PLAINE

Contents

Contents

DARWIN, MARX, and WAGNER

Andreas Dorpalen

Man and His Destiny

The Darwin-Marx-Wagner Debate: 1859–1959

I N THE SPRING of 1859, the very year in which there burst upon the world Darwin's *Origin of Species,* Marx's *Critique of Political Economy,* and Wagner's *Tristan and Isolde,* Alexis de Tocqueville, that sage observer of the Old World and the New passed away. He had felt lonely and misunderstood during the last years of his life. "We belong to a moral and intellectual family that is disappearing," he confided to a friend shortly before the end,[1] and one wonders whether his premature death at the age of fifty-four was not hastened by the feeling that time had passed him by.

In a sense it had. An aristocrat by birth and by taste, yet sensitive to the trends of the times, "balanced," as he put it, "between the past and the future," Tocqueville had viewed the contemporary scene with the detachment of one who felt himself an outsider rather than a participant. Whatever his personal preferences, he understood better than most of his social peers that it had become pointless to wonder whether government by the few was superior to government by the many—society was irresistibly tending toward a broadening of its political basis. The only valid question now was

whether in the approaching age of mass pressures and standards there would emerge a "democracy without poetry or
elevation indeed, but with order and morality," or an equali-
tarian despotism as fatal to human freedom and dignity as
any the world had ever witnessed before.

His American travels had shown him that a democratic
republic could safeguard individual rights, and while he
doubted that its cultural achievements could ever equal those
of a monarchy governed by a social and intellectual elite,
he was willing to grant that the republican form of government had a "nobility of its own." After all, he wryly observed, "it may be God's will to spread a moderate amount
of happiness over all men instead of heaping a large sum
upon a few by allowing only a small minority to approach
perfection." [2]

Yet the viability of the American republic did not guar-
antee the success of a republican-democratic regime in
France. Tocqueville was haunted by the fear that his country-
men lacked those qualities that he felt had assured the effective functioning of the American system of government—
common sense, private morality, and religious faith. Sensing
the approach of a social crisis in France, he had urged his
colleagues in the Chamber of Deputies a few weeks before
the Revolution of 1848 to abandon their social irresponsi-
bility if they were not to be plunged into a revolutionary
abyss. No one heeded his warnings; the general discontent
exploded into revolution, culminating in the June Days rising
of the workers of Paris and finding a seeming solution in the
mass-supported dictatorship of Louis Napoleon Bonaparte,
the future Napoleon III. Tocqueville's remaining years were
darkened by the fear that the dawning age of the masses
would be an age of tyranny.

Perceptive as he was, however, he ignored an essential ele-

ment in the contemporary scene. His mellow wisdom, born of
the sober rationalism of the eighteenth century, could hardly
appeal to the bursting vitality of the 1850's. The forces that
the Industrial Revolution had released were transforming
not only the social and political structure of nations; they
were also reshaping their mentality, invigorating energies
and impulses that had lain dormant in the restrained atmosphere of the Age of Reason. An era to which science
and technology were giving immense new powers was unwilling to listen to the cautious reasoning of a skeptical
rationalist; it insisted on simple, "scientific" answers to its
problems. Few cared to wonder whether human problems
could or should be solved in this manner.

Henry Adams has told us how he first became aware of
these new needs in that very year 1859 in which Tocqueville
died. In his *Education of Henry Adams* he has described
how, as a young student in Germany, "floundering," like
Tocqueville, "between worlds passed and worlds coming,"
he was shaken out of his "eighteenth-century" complacency
by the news of the outbreak of the Austro-Italian War.[3] To a
young American only recently arrived from the ordered
stability of Harvard Yard, the situation must have seemed
confusing indeed. France, under Napoleon III, was helping
the Italians expel the Austrians from northern Italy, the
major part of which the Austrians had controlled since the
Congress of Vienna. Both France and Austria seemed morally
evil to Adams, while Italy, aspiring to unification, clearly
deserved his acclaim. What worried him, nevertheless, was
Italy's decision to choose such a dubious ally as France to
achieve her rightful ambitions. He began to wonder whether
steam power and electricity were transforming the world so
radically that traditional moral principles would have to be
discarded.

In the light of the customary practices of statecraft and
diplomacy, the speculation may seem naïve, yet it had a
basic relevance. Adams sensed that science and technology
were adding a new dimension to the world and that to give
meaning to this changing world, new answers would have to
be found to its problems. He devoted, in fact, the latter part
of his life to this quest for a unifying principle by which
science might provide a solution to the social and moral
chaos which, in his eyes, it was creating. He never found it,[4]
but he did not give up hope that such a principle could be
found and give meaning again to man and his world. In the
concluding sentence of the *Education*, he suggested that were
he allowed to return to earth on his one-hundredth anniversary, in 1938, he might find a world "that sensitive and
timid natures could regard without a shudder."

The sentence makes melancholy reading today, for 1938
was the year of Hitler's annexation of Austria and of the
Munich Conference. A year later World War II broke out.
The world was plunged into this catastrophe largely because
some men thought they had found that basic law for which
Adams had searched in vain in his quest for peace and order.
Insisting that their principle alone gave a new meaning to
life, they or their twentieth-century disciples brought the
world to the verge of that chaos which threatens to engulf all
of us. Darwin, Marx, and Wagner were among the most influential of these thinkers; and since their doctrines, real or
alleged, continue to overshadow our lives, an examination
of their thought and impact is therefore much more than a
mere exercise in intellectual history.

Jacques Barzun, in his evaluation of these three men some
twenty years ago,[5] showed that as social thinkers they were
held together by bonds far stronger than mere contempora-
neousness. All three shared an intellectual affinity that lent

their individual impact additional strength. They pictured man as living in a world ruled by forces with which the individual could not cope and in which the individual mattered only in so far as he served to perpetuate the collectivity to which he belonged—Darwin's species, Marx's class, and Wagner's race. Even these groupings were subject to mechanical laws. Survival, in Darwin's dogma, depended on accidental, unpredictable variations. Marx, in turn, saw man subject to the laws of dialectical materialism, and while he held out hope for man's ultimate liberation from poverty and exploitation, he warned with cool detachment that this goal could be achieved only after the proletariat had suffered even greater misery than before. Wagner, finally, saw mankind doomed in a world of racial and moral decay—a theme around which almost all of his later operas revolve. The world, then, which Darwin, Marx, and Wagner pictured, was a world of mechanical materialism, propelled by impersonal, automatic forces—a world which was amoral and unfeeling, a world without beauty and sensitivity, and one in which art could have no function of its own but could merely serve ulterior social ends. Its task, as Wagner envisaged it, was to provide a release from the hopelessness of human existence.

It was a world at which, in Henry Adams' words, one could only shudder, and one wonders why so large a part of mankind could ever feel at home in it. The fact is that no one did. For the world which men entered, following these guides, was not one in which they were helplessly carried along by a primordial uncontrollable destiny, but one in which they expected to be masters of their fate or able, at least, to exalt it. It was this hope, held out in each case at the price of striking doctrinal inconsistencies, that explains the ascendancy of these three men.

Of the three, Darwin achieved the most immediate influence. His great scientific contribution was in the realm of the theory of evolution, but it was his theory of natural selection that spread his influence far beyond the field of biology. This latter doctrine provided for the social and economic practices of the upper classes a scientific justification that had so far been lacking. This was the time in which the Industrial Revolution was reaching its peak in Britain, in which it was gathering momentum in the United States, France, Belgium, and Prussia, in which nationalism was changing from a sense of community with one's fellow nationals into aggressive feelings of superiority over other nations. It was a time of great vigor, of bursting energies seeking new outlets and opportunities, of an adventurous optimism striking out on paths never before explored. But it was also an age of great ruthlessness, of human exploitation and degradation, in which the success of a few was bought with the misery of untold millions.

For this flaw Darwin provided, or was claimed to provide, a scientific alibi. It was summed up succinctly in the famous concluding paragraph of the *Origin* which pictured the existing forms of life as the result of

a Ratio of Increase so high as to lead to a Struggle for Life, and as a consequence to Natural Selection, entailing Divergence of Character and the Extinction of less-improved forms. Thus, from the war of nature, from famine and death, the most exalted object which we are capable of conceiving, namely, the production of the higher animals, directly follows. There is grandeur in this view of life, with its several powers, having been originally breathed by the Creator into a few forms or into one; and that, whilst this planet has gone cycling on according to the fixed law of gravity, from so simple a beginning endless forms most beautiful and most wonderful have been, and are being evolved.

If this was the way of nature, it was right and indeed "natural" for businessmen to exploit their workers, to ruin their competitors, and to charge the consumer whatever the traffic would bear. Darwin's doctrine provided also a welcome underpinning for imperialist expansion, which was now justified as the inevitable victory of superior over inferior people, and it offered a new rationale for war as man's finest test.

None of this actually followed from Darwin's theory, which said nothing more than that those best equipped to survive do survive. These survivors, however, are not necessarily fighters, either in the word's literal or figurative meaning, but may well be those, in Jacques Barzun's words, who are content to sit tight and endure. But Darwin, who preferred a dramatic though imprecise turn of phrase to an accurate but colorless turn, chose to describe the process of mere survival in terms of a struggle for existence and to explain the outcome of this struggle as the result of a process of natural selection rather than simple preservation. Admittedly, he claimed to speak only in metaphors,[6] but the second one especially was quite misleading, for it suggested that nature possessed that quality of purposeful selection the denial of which was the very essence of the Darwinian doctrine. It was this inconsistency, of course, to which that doctrine owed its enthusiastic acceptance, for it encouraged the belief that survival was a reward that went only to those who deserved it.

Emphasis on the element of struggle was misleading also because it discounted the importance of co-operation, a factor which Darwin himself had recognized to be an essential basis of human relations. Yet in the competitive world in which he lived, Darwin viewed co-operation simply as a way for social groups—families, tribes, nations—to improve their competitive position. If co-operation benefited the indi-

vidual, Darwin considered such help a fortuitous dividend of
no intrinsic significance. He was concerned with the survival
of the species rather than with that of its individual members; besides, he believed that such co-operation would primarily benefit those individuals who were actually least de-
serving of survival.[7]

Whatever the flaws in his reasoning, these very flaws made
it immensely attractive to those to whose actions Darwinian
arguments would now lend an aura of respectability. If anything, business practices became more ruthless, imperialist
expansion more uninhibited, nationalism more chauvinist under the Darwinian impact.)

(If social Darwinism provided the Magna Charta for the upper classes of the Industrial Age, Marxism addressed itself to
those whom the Industrial Revolution had plunged into bleak
misery.)The factory system, the growing size of industrial
enterprises, the transformation of human labor into a com-
modity whose value was determined by the law of supply and
demand, and, last but not least, the rapidly spreading urban-
ization of the industrial nations had left the workers with the
tormenting feeling that their life was dominated by powerful,
uncontrollable forces condemning them to a life of permanent misery) While the craftsman of earlier times had been
the master of his work and a creator, the factory worker of
the Industrial Age was but a servant in a process that became
ever more complex and unintelligible to him.(Impotent, help-
less, encased in a rigid class system from which there was no
escaping, the Continental worker could derive no comfort
from Darwinism, for there seemed to be every indication that
he was not fit to survive the competitive struggle.) He readily
turned to Marx, therefore, when the latter told him that the
very forces which were holding him in bondage were leading

to the destruction of the bourgeoisie and to the ultimate liberation of the proletariat. In terms of the Darwinian struggle
for existence in which Marx saw a welcome naturalist con-
firmation of his own theory of the class struggle, the proletariat, then, was much fitter to survive than was the bourgeoisie.

Marx accepted the Darwinian doctrine the more readily
since he was convinced that men were as much subject to "natural" laws as were any physical phenomena. Such was, in
fact, their subjection to the laws of dialectical materialism
that they could not defy its operations. There was no chance,
therefore, as he saw it, that capitalists could ever mend their
ways and cease exploiting workers. He was aware of the possibility of social reforms—the Factory Acts had been enacted
in England before the completion of the first volume of *Das
Kapital*—but he was convinced that where such reforms
could not be evaded, they would serve merely to accelerate
the process of capitalist concentration. The burdens they
placed on the smaller enterprises would render the latter unable to compete with the larger ones and drive them out of
business.[8] (It is indicative of the pervasive naturalist spirit of
the times that while Marx considered capitalists constitution-
ally incapable, as it were, of mending their ways, anti-Marx-
ists, such as Treitschke, the German historian, had similar
reservations about what might be called the biological fitness
of the workers to rise above their lowly status.) [9] Marx's mistaken belief that man was irretrievably tied to the dictates of
dialectical materialism explains why he proved so poor a
prophet in many of his prognoses.[10]

Like Darwin, moreover, Marx was basically inconsistent in
what he taught, and as in Darwin's case, it was this very inconsistency which made his views palatable. While he considered man subject to the laws of dialectical materialism, he
also believed that man could escape this bondage by turning

over all means of production to the proletarian state. Yet he
never even considered the possibility that dialectical materialism might continue to "operate" even then, and that those
wielding power in it might assume the role of the dethroned
capitalist.

Nor did Marx show greater perception in his forecasts
about the middle class. Contrary to his expectations, those of
its members who succumbed to the rigors of capitalist competition were not driven into the ranks of the proletariat, but
retained their social identity. Yet, as victims of capitalism,
these men also felt exposed to sinister forces from which they
could not escape, and longed for release from a life over
which they seemed to have lost all control. They found allies
in others not hurt economically, who saw their traditional
world collapse under the onslaught of the new industrial and
commercial forces. Officials and officers, clergy and academi-
cians, landowners, and members of the professions, all felt
their social and political prerogatives threatened by business
and labor. Unable (or unwilling) to adjust themselves to the
existence of these new elements, they haughtily kept aloof
from them. They preferred to indulge in emotional mystiques
and to bemoan the corrupting materialism of the industrial
age. A series of financial scandals lent strong support to these
allegations. The impact of these frauds was especially
marked in Germany, which had plunged into industrial and
commercial expansion with exceptional vigor, but was not
sufficiently flexible and self-assured to absorb the emerging
new classes into its social and political structure. As a result,
fierce outbursts of antiliberalism and anti-Semitism shook
the country during the 1870's and 80's. Similar difficulties
arose in Austria and Russia and became a serious problem
also in France, as the Dreyfus Affair demonstrated.

⟨The work of Richard Wagner reflects this frustration and disillusionment of preindustrial society.⟩Many of his operas gave forceful expression to its rebellion against the ascendancy of business, and by lending these emotions the power of his dramatic and musical gifts, Wagner helped raise them to the rarefied level of a *Weltanschauung*.⟨Unlike Marx and Darwin, he did not welcome as progress the technical and economic advances of the nineteenth century, but saw in them primarily symptoms of a shallow materialism.⟩As a young man, in 1848, he had stood on Dresden's barricades to fight the "Philistine" bourgeoisie, and he had kept assailing the corruption and degradation of life in both his writings and operas after the collapse of that rising.⟨The dominant theme of most of his operas is that of a world ruined by greed and deceit in which the hero succumbs to the forces of evil. In his writings Wagner saw these forces embodied in a materialist civilization that catered to man's lowest instincts and whose corrupting influence was aided and abetted by the capitalist system. He tinged this anticapitalism with strong anti-Semitic overtones, thus giving concrete embodiment to the target of his attacks.⟩

For these latter views Wagner found welcome support in the racial theories of Count Gobineau, the French publicist, whose *Essay on the Inequality of the Human Races* was a first attempt to view history as the product of racial laws that determined the fate of mankind. Gobineau's approach, too, was characteristic of that uninhibited application of scientific, or allegedly scientific, methods to human relations which was so marked a trend of that era. One scholar has summed up his contemporary significance by saying that he "boasted of having introduced history into the family of natural sciences, detected the natural law of all courses of events, reduced all

spiritual utterances or cultural phenomena to something 'that
by virtue of exact science our eyes can see, our ears can hear,
our hands can touch.' " [11] No approach to man's problems
could have been more materialistic, and it is indicative of
Wagner's intellectual confusion that he who was so determined to fight the materialism of his time eagerly seized upon
Gobineau's theories to achieve his objective.

Racial theories had of course existed prior to the publication of Gobineau's *Essay*, and anti-Jewish attitudes had been
widespread before Wagner voiced them; but their combination into racial anti-Semitism was novel and fateful in its effects. Earlier anti-Jewish reactions had been based on religious or emotional grounds, possibly also on economic ones,
but as such they implied the possibility of Jewish "redemption"—either by baptism or by the abandonment of traits or
practices that were considered objectionable. What gave the
new racial anti-Semitism its distinctive character was that it
excluded all possibility of change. It viewed Jewish "inferiority" as a biological fact beyond human control, the result of a law as immutable as Marx's dialectical materialism
which propelled the bourgeoisie into its inevitable self-
destruction.

Wagner warned, however, that unlike the Germans the Jews
had retained their racial "purity." They were, therefore, bio-
logically stronger than the Germans, and since the Germans'
racial decay could not be arrested, the latter, he was convinced, lacked the strength to assert their rightful ascendancy
over the Jews. Yet like Darwin and Marx, Wagner, too, allowed for an escape from his gloomy diagnosis. Despite their
racial degeneration, the Germans, he felt, had retained an
artistic sensitivity that could grant them at least a temporary
release from the sordid reality of everyday life. Through the
medium of art they could hope to attain a purified life even

in a doomed and tragic world, so that race, though presumably all-pervasive, would cease to matter. By helping man to transcend the hopelessness of life and develop a new ethics of love and compassion,[12] art was to assume the role of religion, and the artist would become the Germans' new priest.[13]

To serve as "life's kindly savior," Wagner insisted that art be ruthlessly realistic.[14] While creating a world of illusions, it must yet picture this dream world in the full harshness of the corrupt, passion-driven real world. For he believed that art could provide a respite from despair only if it were believable and that it would defeat its noblest purpose were it to indulge in innocuous fairy tales. In the gloomy world of his operas even the heroes are apt therefore to be cheats or adulterers. (The most important exception, of course, is *Parsifal*, the herald of the new ethics of compassionate love, but Parsifal, the "pure fool," so alien to Wagner's true nature, has something strikingly contrived and unreal about him.) [15] While Wagner's masterful art offered release from the bleakness of life, the prescription was of the type to breed a corrosive moral and social cynicism rather than inspire a new morality.

This was not at once evident. By and large, the half-century before World War I was one of great prosperity. The crises which shook it did produce unsavory reactions, but these receded when economic conditions improved once more. Nor did Marxism remain unaffected by the increase in wealth; the working class, too, began to enjoy the benefits of industrial growth. At the same time, the upper classes relented in their Darwinian interpretation of the social scene; uncertain about whether they could retain their position in the face of the workers' growing strength, they sought to protect themselves by social and political concessions. Marxists, therefore,

tended to abandon the militant features of their program and
began to put their faith in parliamentary methods.

But the old dogmas were not completely submerged in the
mellowness of the "Golden Age." They survived as under-
currents, feeding the continued spiritual malaise of the time,
and found some new highly articulate spokesmen in such men
as Lenin, who upheld and sharpened the doctrine of revolutionary Marxism, and Houston Stewart Chamberlain, Wagner's son-in-law, who propounded and elaborated the latter's
racist and social views.

Beyond the realm of theory, the three doctrines affected,
and in turn derived new impulses from, the imperialist wave
then sweeping across the world. Imperialism, in fact, appeared to represent a literal application of all three dogmas.[16] Unlike earlier colonial ventures, imperialist acqui-
sitions did not, except incidentally, serve the traditional
objectives of settlement and colonization. They aimed at supposedly higher purposes—the strengthening of the acquiring
power's military position (Egypt, Hawaii), the protection of
property rights (Malaya, Latin America), or expansion simply for expansion's sake (Cecil Rhodes). Imperialist advances thus were undertaken for reasons not directly concerned with the territory in question—a significant parallel
to the economic phenomenon of production for production's
rather than consumption's sake and another example of man's
alienation from the purposes and products of his work. Imperialism, in consequence, was eagerly seized upon by Marxists—critically, as a further demonstration of the rapacious
nature of the capitalist system; hopefully, as leading inevitably to war over clashing expansionist ambitions and thus
hastening its own downfall. But imperialism also bore Darwinist-racist traits. Colonial administrators tended to look on
their native charges as lower breeds and displayed toward

them an aloofness that was the product of a strongly felt superiority rather than of intentional cruelty.)

(This indifference toward one's fellow men was evident, too, in the Continental variety of imperialism.) Its two most important manifestations were the Pan-German and Pan-Slav movements. They displayed the same Darwinist-racist characteristics: the Pan-Germans insisted on meting out to Europe's "inferior" nationalities the same treatment to which overseas imperialism was subjecting native populations. And the Russian Pan-Slavs, asserting their own superiority, called for a crusade against the West to rescue their fellow Slavs from its corrupting influence. If not as immediately successful as overseas imperialism, the Continental type proved more dangerous in the long run because the impact of its human and moral corrosion was not weakened by geographical distance. Nor were the Continental imperialists restrained by political traditions or values. Whatever the abuses in the British Empire or in America's possessions, public opinion obtained their eventual correction. German public opinion was much less effective, and so was Russia's. Pan-Germanism and Pan-Slavism were reservoirs, then, of attitudes of ominous potentialities.

Imperialism, it need hardly be said, was the antipode of all laissez faire policies, and its sweeping advance hastened the latter's departure. Social thought did not escape the effects of this change; neither did the doctrines of our three thinkers which had been instrumental in bringing it about. Darwin, Marx, and Wagner had adhered to the laissez faire approach at least in the sense that they rejected all interference with the laws they believed they had discovered. Darwin had been content to trace the laws of evolution and selection, but he could not predict who specifically would emerge as the fittest. Nor was he willing to narrow down the area of uncertainty by do-

ing away with the unfit, and he condemned all forcible attempts to prevent the survival and propagation of the "socially undesirable." [17] (Yet many of his disciples were not
satisfied with such resignation, and they developed out of his
theories the science of eugenics which seeks to improve on the
slow and "inefficient" process of "natural selection" by such
means as birth and marriage control, sterilization, or the systematic breeding of a better race.)

Marxism underwent a similar transformation. Marx was
convinced that the change of the economy from capitalism to
communism was an automatic process. While the working
class ought to prepare for the day when the time would be
"ripe" for the proletarian revolution, there was little it could
do to hasten its advent. The evolutionary Marxists were not
the only ones to reject this resignation, relying on parliamentary methods to speed up the process of socialization; the advocates of revolutionary Marxism did also. (Lenin insisted
that effective organization and timely action could precipitate the overthrow of bourgeois society; and when he struck
in 1917, he was not entirely sure that the situation, while tac-
tically promising, was "ripe" in the doctrinal sense.[18]

Wagner's social and racial theories, too, assumed a more
"activist" character at the hands of his disciples. He had been
convinced, we recall, that the disintegration of the German
nation was inevitable because of its advanced racial decay.
Yet Houston Stewart Chamberlain, his spiritual heir, rejected the fatalism of his father-in-law and insisted that this
decline was far from inevitable. "A noble race does not fall
from heaven," he maintained in his *Foundations of the Nineteenth Century*, "but it becomes noble gradually, just like
fruit trees, and this process can get under way at any moment,
as soon as a geographical-historical chance or a systematic
plan . . . provide the necessary conditions." What was es-

sential was that suitable "material" be available (his contemputous reference to human beings as "material" is revealing), and joining hands with the most radical advocates of eugenics, he asserted that such material could then be perfected by "selective breeding." "One can best understand this method by studying the principles of artificial breeding in the animal and vegetable kingdom; . . . there are few things which so enrich our knowledge of the plastic potentialities of life." An essential part of this breeding process would of course consist in the elimination of all inferior "material"; by way of illustration he pointed approvingly to the custom of abandoning weakly infants, which Greeks, Romans, and Germans had practiced in ancient times.[19]

Chamberlain was not only convinced that the German race could thus be saved and ennobled; he was equally certain that once it had overcome its racial decay it could, by means of a scientific organization of its entire national life, secure the domination of the world.

> By scientific organization [he wrote] I mean the application of scientific principles that have produced such unparalleled achievements in Germany in science and technology, possibly also in public administration; as another illustration I mention the painstaking precision in the use of existing means so that a maximum result can be achieved at minimum cost and the available resources multiplied a hundredfold, also a division of labor assigning everyone to the task he can do best and for which he is best suited—all this requires efficient planning, that is, a systematic integration of all parts in all fields of activity. . . . A race-conscious Germany, excluding everything unGerman in its government. . . . integrated politically from its center to its most remote corners and inspired by one uniform purpose . . . would thus be able, due to its physical power and the nobility of its spirit, to rule the world, despite its numerical inferiority to both Anglo-Saxons and Russians.[20]

Evidently, in this blueprint of a more efficient and powerful Germany the individual, stripped of all rights and aspirations of his own, was expected to all but lose his human identity.

In a stable, orderly world this brazen challenge of man's humanity would have had little effect, even though Chamberlain's books were best-sellers in Germany as piquant intellectual fare. World War I, however, so disrupted the spiritual and material foundations of Germany and Europe that in the ensuing chaos Hitler could translate these cerebrations into a fearful reality. This he did with a literalness that has rarely if ever been equaled in the history of ideas. He could do so because he himself lived his own life, physically and mentally, in a Wagnerian world of decay and corruption in which reality and imagination blended into an inseparable entity.[21]

Considering himself essentially an artist and an architect, Hitler set out literally to rebuild the world. (The phrase is his and is repeatedly used in *Mein Kampf*.) Contemptuous of the rationalism of liberal democracy, he agreed with Wagner, and, for that matter, with Nietzsche whom he otherwise misunderstood, that only artistic intuition and imagination, unhampered by bourgeois conventions, could save Germany from utter decay and destruction. This saving mission he wanted to carry out exactly as Chamberlain had envisaged it —by the breeding of a new German race and the mass killings of "undesirables," by the rigid organization of all available human "material," a term he used as uninhibitedly as his mentor, and the wholesale shifting of populations. Many of these plans he carried out while in power; in his informal table talks of which records have been preserved he painted a terrifying picture of the kind of Europe he proposed to build after he had won the war. An irrepressible impulse to fight, a compulsion that literally drove him into wars, lent these plans a momentum which for a time seemed irresistible.

(In this twilight world of social and biological engineering where the distinction between human nature and animal instincts was becoming blurred, the phenomenon of Hitler gains added significance from his striking physiological affinity to the world of his spiritual mentors. In Wagner's operas the predominant scenery is one of craggy mountains and dark forests, of treacherous ravines and gloomy caves. It was re-created in the physical environment in which Hitler felt most at home. He had a strong aversion to sunshine, preferred dark and dank quarters, and felt happiest in cool misty weather. He chose the Berghof near Berchtesgaden as his favorite retreat because it met all these requirements. Since it was built on the northern slope of the Obersalzberg, hardly a ray of sunshine ever reached it, and its solid walls kept it cold even in warm weather. Similarly, Wagner had a marked preference for the night as the time for dramatic action. The day, Tristan declares, is filled with greed and envy, with toil and vicissitude; it is the time of the mind, of reason and logic. The night, on the other hand, is given to passion and emotion:

> During the day, spent in vain hope,
> All that is left is that sweet longing,
> That longing for the sacred night
> Where eternally,
> Genuinely
> Rapturous love
> Awaits us.

Night, then, is the time when love promises release and salvation. But behind the sensual overtones, the night is greeted

also as the liberator from conventional loyalties and obliga-
tions; for Tristan, wooing Isolde under cover of night, vio-
lates the oath of fealty he has sworn to King Mark. That
Hitler was a man of the night, becoming almost a different
person as dark set in, more alert and vicacious, saving his
most important work for the late evening and keeping his
entourage up until the small hours of the morning, is a matter of record. Representing what it did in Wagner's world,
the night did indeed suit Hitler's personality far better than
the day.

Many comparisons with Russia suggest themselves in the
aforesaid; but Soviet problems will be discussed in other papers, and I shall pursue here only one possible parallel. Hitler and Stalin resembled each other in many ways—in their
indifference to individual suffering, in their inhumane dis-
posal of human lives, in their cynicism and deviousness, and
in their efforts to reshape man. Race breeding as practiced in
Nazi Germany was echoed in Stalin's support of Lysenko's
biological theories. For if acquired characteristics could be
passed on to subsequent generations, Soviet man could indeed
be remolded like the Nazi Aryan. What is of special interest
in this context is the fact that Stalin, too, was a man of the
night; his working day did not start, as a rule, before the late
afternoon. And if Hitler derived a basic satisfaction from in-
volving himself in ever new fights, Stalin seems to have
derived a sensual pleasure from revenging himself on his
enemies. "To choose one's victim, to prepare one's plans minutely, to slake an implacable vengeance, and then to go to
bed," he is said to have told two associates, "there is nothing
sweeter in the world." [22] We know too little about his personal traits and habits beyond these few data to pursue this
parallel further, but future historians may well find that the
efforts to determine man's fate "scientifically" reached their

disastrous climax when seized upon by men who showed even in their physiological make-up how fluid the dividing line had become between human qualities and animal impulses.

This attempt to analyze the social impact of Darwin, Marx, and Wagner would not be complete without at least a brief quest for the reasons why these doctrines were not everywhere equally influential. I shall limit myself to an examination of the reception they have had in this country.

Of the three doctrines, social Darwinism was the only one that was widely accepted here. Not only did it provide a scientific underpinning for prevailing business practices, but it also seemed to confirm the hope of those at the bottom of the social and economic ladder that, given ability and determination, they, too, could rise to the top. In the face of this deep-rooted faith, Darwinism as a social theory survived here longer than it did in most other countries. (Its widespread acceptance helps to explain in turn why Marxism with its emphasis on unbridgeable class differences appealed to so few Americans.) But in the end, here, too, social Darwinism had to yield ground to modifying social reforms—to a more equitable distribution of opportunities and to the reassurance of some measure of social security. And in effecting these reforms the nation countered whatever following Marxism may have gained here during the disheartening years of the Great Depression.

The most important opposition to the social applications of Darwinism issued, we know, from the churches. Religious criticism, it is true, was directed primarily against Darwin's theory of evolution, which is so obviously at variance with the Genesis version of creation; yet aside from such fundamentalist condemnation, many religious groups objected to that theory also on the grounds that it was incompatible with the spiritual nature of man. This it was not, for Darwin was explaining only the "how" of human evolution, not the "why" or the "wherefore" which is the concern of religion. But his religious opponents, as we have since learned, did sense a grave and real danger—that Darwin's theories might lend themselves to inhuman applications for which they were never intended. (And Darwin's own ambiguities did admittedly leave the door open to such abuses.)

If Wagnerism in the social-political sense never received much attention in this country, the reason, again, is to be found in the special circumstances of the American experience. Americans, as Tocqueville already noted, have always preferred a pragmatic approach to politics. There was no need here to wonder about the destiny of man, à la Hegel, Spengler, or Wagner, for destiny was "manifest." Nor could a philosophy of doom and disaster culminating in a vague socialist-humanitarian utopia provide a solution to America's racial problems. Those few individuals who did derive some inspiration from Wagner and his twentieth-century disciples received, therefore, little attention except for a fleeting moment during the turbulent Nazi era.

The totalitarian systems that have evolved out of the doctrines of our three thinkers thus have held little attraction for Americans. But the quick confidence with which these theories could once be dismissed is giving way now to a growing uneasiness in the face of the Communist challenge. For this powerful threat is aimed at the very core of the American way of life, and is, therefore, a crucial test of its basic vitality. Whether America will meet it will depend essentially on her continued faith in her own way of life. She has been determined so far to reject the precepts of Marxism and Wagnerism (or Naziism) and has reduced the influence of social Darwinism to a healthy modicum. Despite painful lapses into political conformity and ideological rigidity, she thus continues to be guided by the belief that man, in Max Lerner's words, is a "bundle of potentials" and that his potentialities can best be developed by himself. Within the context of this approach, state and society are to assist such self-realization, but with the basic qualification that any political or social organization seeking to further these aspirations must be, to quote Max Lerner once more, "instrumental" rather than "central." [23]

Man, then, has in this view some measure of control over his fate and is not merely the object of inexorable naturalist, dialectical, or racial laws. As long as this faith in man survives and men prove themselves worthy of this faith, Marx, Darwin, and Wagner are not likely to become the ultimate masters of the destiny of man.

1. *Memoirs, Letters, and Remains of Alexis de Tocqueville* (Cambridge and London, 1861), II, 466.

2. *Ibid.*, II, 31, I, 397–98.

3. *The Education of Henry Adams: An Autobiography* (New York, 1942), pp. 78–79.

4. By applying the second law of thermodynamics to history, he did, however, arrive at the conclusion that human thought would reach the "limit of its possibilities" in the year 1921, or, as he was cautious enough to add, at the latest in 2025 (Henry Adams, "The Rule of Phase Applied to History," in *The Degradation of the Democratic Dogma* [New York, 1949], p. 308).

5. Jacques Barzun, *Darwin, Marx, Wagner: Critique of a Heritage* (Boston, 1941).

6. *The Origin of Species by Means of Natural Selection or the Preservation of Favored Races in the Struggle for Life and the Descent of Man and Selection in Relation to Sex* (New York, 1936), pp. 52, 64.

7. *Ibid.*, pp. 52, 56–57, 471 ff., 498–99, 501–2.

8. Karl Marx, *Capital: A Critique of Political Economy* (Chicago, 1932), I, 552.

9. Andreas Dorpalen, *Heinrich von Treitschke* (New Haven, 1957), pp. 202–3.

10. Ironically, Marx's effectiveness as a social critic also helped to refute him. By arousing the workers in the industrial nations to an awareness of their strength, he enabled them to obtain major concessions from the upper classes and to improve their lot without the complete destruction of the capitalist system. As a result there did not occur in these countries that radical transformation of society and economy which he had considered inevitable.

11. Hannah Arendt, *The Origins of Totalitarianism* (New York, 1951), p. 171.

12. Cf. Lenin's remark to Maxim Gorky, after listening to Beethoven's *Apassionata:* "I can't listen to music too often. It affects your nerves, makes you want to say stupid nice things and stroke the heads of people who could create such beauty while living in this vile hell. And now you mustn't stroke anyone's head. . . ."—Quoted in Frederick L. Schuman, *Soviet Politics at Home and Abroad* (New York, 1946), p. 184. Wagner, it should be added, always felt that Beethoven's music came closer to his own than that of any other composer. See his article on Beethoven in his *Gesammelte Schriften und Dichtungen* (Leipzig, 1898), IX, 61–126, esp. 83 ff.; also Paul Bekker, *Richard Wagner: His Life and His Work* (New York, 1931), pp. 402 ff.

13. Richard Wagner, "Religion und Kunst," *loc. cit.*, X, 211–88.

14. "Ueber Staat und Religion," *ibid.*, VIII, 28–9.

15. Cf. Barzun, *op. cit.*, p. 309; Bekker, *op. cit.*, p. 485; Kurt Hildebrandt, *Wagner und Nietzsche: Ihr Kampf gegen das neunzehnte Jahrhundert* (Breslau, 1924), pp. 373 ff.

16. For the following, cf. Arendt, *op. cit.*, Part II.

17. Darwin, *op. cit.*, pp. 501–2.

18. Lenin's doubts were not caused by Russia's industrial backwardness. Like Marx, he believed that Russia need not necessarily go through the bourgeois-industrial phase before a socialist revolution could be launched, provided there were simultaneous revolutions in the West, and these he believed imminent. But he was not entirely certain in the fall of 1917 whether the disintegration of the upper and middle classes had sufficiently advanced to ensure the permanent victory of the Bolsheviks.

19. Houston Stewart Chamberlain, *Die Grundlagen des XIX. Jahrhunderts* (Munich, 1907), pp. 314, 327–28.

20. *Politische Ideale* (F. Bruckmann KG, Munich, 1915), pp. 77, 88–89; the last sentence Chamberlain wrote originally in a letter (to

Emperor William II?) in November, 1902. Translated by the author and used by permission of the publisher.

21. For the following, cf. Andreas Dorpalen, "Hitler—Twelve Years After," *Review of Politics*, XIX (1957), 486–506, esp. 492, 501–3, 505–6.

22. Boris Souvarine, *Stalin: A Critique of Bolshevism* (New York, 1939), p. 485.

23. Max Lerner, *America as a Civilization: Life and Thought in the United States Today* (New York, 1957), pp. 945, 946.

Bentley Glass

Darwinism in Modern Biology

THE HISTORIAN OF SCIENCE, of the history of ideas—I hope even a biologist may be counted among such—is interested in the phenomenon of Darwin—his ideas and their contribution to scientific thought. It is in no sense derogatory to the life and achievement of a great man to recognize that, like all of us, he had some very human characteristics, or that his thoughts always developed out of the cultural past of his time and his people, and reflected variously the atmosphere of his own civilization. In this respect, as Jacques Barzun so well pointed out twenty years ago, Darwin was a child of his time—but to say that is in no way to diminish his stature.

In the past two years, during the celebration of the centennial of *The Origin of Species,* some things have been said about the sources of Darwin's ideas—about his forerunners and about the way Darwin put his ideas together—that have been severely criticized by those who almost worship the thought of the great man and who regard as derogatory any intimation that his every thought did not spring full-fledged from his own inspired brain. I assure you that Darwin was as human as the rest of us and got his ideas here and there; and very often he was not able afterward to tell you where he got them. In fact, he was really very deficient in the historical sense, as Barzun has pointed out, and did not keep very good notes on the sources of his own information and inspiration. Much of what he tells us about the origins of his thought is incomplete, imperfect, and perhaps even misguided.

Let us take a quick look at Darwin's achievement in order to refresh our memories, for it may be some years since we sat in a biology classroom and heard an explanation of his theory of organic evolution. Darwin is generally given credit for having done two things: first, for having set forth the theory of organic evolution, that is, the evolution of each species from an antecedent species, and, ultimately, from one or a very few original forms; and, second, for being the first to propose a satisfactory explanation of how the origination of species occurs. This explanation is the theory of natural selection. We must distinguish quite carefully between the theory of evolution, as such, and the theory of natural selection, which is concerned with the means or mechanisms involved in the evolutionary process.

What Darwin did with respect to the first of these two achievements was simply to set forth, far more completely and accurately and cogently than had ever been done before, all the known evidences for organic evolution and the origin of species. The theory itself was not new with him. It was an old, old theory. It had been extensively discussed for more than a hundred years, and adumbrations of such ideas can be traced back to remote antiquity. The evidences that Darwin assembled, and which proved so convincing to his fellow biologists, as well as to the general public, may be subsumed under five categories.

First, there exists a unity of structural plan in various species, a unity which was taken to be an indication of their nearness of relationship. This idea of unity of plan was a very old one. It was the basis of the conception of the "Great Chain of Being," about which Arthur O. Lovejoy has written so fully. It does not necessarily involve the idea of evolution at all. Similarities of body plan may exist among different animals without their having evolved from one another. The same is true of plants. In fact, one of the greatest British biologists, a contemporary of Darwin, Richard Owen, first gave this particular likeness a name, homology. Thus the front limb of a man, the arm, is homologous in its structure, and corresponds in each segment, piece by piece, with the front limb of a dog or a cat, or, of course, a monkey. Yet Owen himself, to the end of his life, remained a bitter opponent of the idea that these resemblances are to be regarded as evidences of evolution. In 1830, a great debate took place between Georges Cuvier and Geoffroy Saint-Hilaire about the meaning of this unity of plan in the living world. Saint-Hilaire took the part of the evolutionary interpretation and Cuvier denied it. Evidently, there was nothing unique about this category of Darwin's evidences of evolution.

Another category of evidences of evolution was derived from a study of developmental processes, the nature of the growth and development of living things. These evidences we find particularly well illustrated among the higher animals, where embryonic resemblances had long been observed. The great German biologist Karl Ernst von Baer, in the early years of the nineteenth century, had remarked that the examination of a considerable variety of vertebrate animals had shown that the embryos resemble one another much more in the very early than in later stages of their life histories. As development continues, likenesses disappear. He is reputed to have told the story that in two separate vials of pickling fluid he had two little embryos that had not been labeled, and after some years he was unable to tell which embryo was that of one animal and which was that of a quite different one. Meckel, another German biologist, had emphasized this same observation, early in the nineteenth century, and had actually given it an evolutionary interpretation. Darwin simply gathered these evidences, known for many decades before his own time, and presented them more fully, more clearly, and more accurately than anyone else had done.

In this same category of evidences stand the rudimentary and vestigial organs, so abundant in adult animals and in the embryonic stages of life as well. The existence of the tail in many forms of vertebrates which are tailless when adult, including, of course, our own species; the presence of the clefts in the sides of the throat in the development of land vertebrates, which remind one of the developing gill slits in a fish; the presence in the human being of muscles in the ear and attached to the ear which exactly resemble in location and form of attachment those found in the donkey and mule, and which in those animals are very useful indeed in cupping the ear and turning it in the direction of a sound, but which in man are of use only for parlor entertainment—these conditions, too, Darwin assembled as evidences of organic evolution.

Third, there were the evidences from historical geology, based in particular on the work done by Charles Lyell, whose conclusions had so profoundly influenced Darwin himself when, as a young man, he traveled around the world on the "Beagle." The geological evidence indicated an earth of greatly extended age; it included the presence of fossils of many different species which could be related by their similarities to forms living today and could be best interpreted on an evolutionary basis. Darwin acknowledged the existence of many gaps, or "missing links," in this picture; and he was critical in pointing out that although we might hope that in the future the sequences of types would gradually become more and more complete, there would probably always remain lacunae, gaps that would never be filled.

The fourth category of evidence was derived from geographical distribution. Darwin himself had been very much impressed on his voyage around the world by the characteristic differences of the animals and birds on the Galapagos Islands, some hundreds of miles off the coast of South America, in the equatorial latitudes. The Galapagos are volcanic islands, and the forms of life found on them, he thought, had not been there for a very long period of time since they rather strikingly resembled birds and mammals that he had but recently seen on the South American mainland in Peru. Nevertheless, he was struck by the fact that they were different—in some respects, startlingly different. The typical finches of the Galapagos differed from island to island. Although they all seemed to be rather like the finches of Peru, some of them were bigger and some smaller; some of them ate cactus seeds, some pecked holes in the cactus pads, and some of them even used cactus spines to dig insects out of their hiding places. These last had habits like a woodpecker that, lacking a suitable bill, had adapted a tool for the purpose of food-gathering. Darwin was much impressed by these differences between the Galapagos fauna and the fauna of the mainland of South America.

Earlier in his voyage Darwin had touched at the Cape Verde Islands, lying on the equator a relatively short distance offshore from the west coast of Africa. The Cape Verde Islands were in nearly every respect—geographically, climatically, and meteorologically—like the Galapagos Islands. If a wise Creator had planned to create types of plants and animals that were adapted to particular sorts of environments, surely he would have put exactly the same kinds of plants and animals and birds on the Cape Verde Islands and the Galapagos, for the two environments are almost identical. But the animals and plants, the insects and birds, of the Cape

Verde Islands are not like those of the Galapagos. They hardly resemble them at all, but are very similar to those found on the mainland of Africa. It was these facts that first led Darwin to think about the formation of new species from old ones in some kind of adjustment to changed climate and changed conditions of life. It was this that actually became in his own mind the germ of a belief in evolution—this together with geological studies that he made in the spirit of Lyell while he was on the South American part of his journey.

The fifth category of evidences for evolution was discussed very imperfectly and very hesitantly by Darwin himself. These were the evidences derived from a knowledge of heredity. Darwin says very early in *The Origin of Species* that unless differences are hereditary, they have no significance for his theory. He was, therefore, very deeply interested in the nature of heredity. He spent a great deal of time studying hereditary variations, but arrived at no satisfactory knowledge of how characteristics are inherited. He was not acquainted with the work that Mendel even then had begun in far-off Bohemia. Later, one of his critics, an engineer named Fleeming Jenkin, put his finger on this weak spot in Darwin's theory of evolution. Jenkin pointed out that if inheritance was what Darwin himself supposed it to be and what it was generally thought to be at the time, a kind of permanent and perpetual blending of whatever characteristics were present in the parents, then the variations present in any generation would rapidly disappear through the blending process. How then could they serve to become the origin of new species as Darwin supposed? Darwin realized then that in every generation there must be an origin of *new* hereditary variations more than sufficient to replace whatever was lost. Being at a loss to account for this, he lapsed into a belief in the inheritance of acquired characteristics. In other words, he thought the environment it-self might produce new hereditary characteristics in living or-ganisms—if it worked over a sufficient length of time. Back in the eighteenth century, a scientist named Pierre Louis de Maupertuis, who was head of Frederick the Great's Academy of Sciences in Berlin, had actually made a study of hereditary variations in the human species. He had studied the inherit-ance in a Berlin family of a condition producing six fingers and six toes on hands and feet, and had shown quite conclu-sively that this deformity did not disappear with time, that it could be passed down either through the male parent or the female parent, and that it was not something that was simply produced by the environment, even if modifiable by it. Mau-pertuis was thus led to develop a view that heredity is not a blending, as of bloods or fluids, but depends upon particles from the parents which assort themselves in the body of the offspring, endure there until another generation is to be pro-duced, and then are passed on again as permanent entities of a hereditary nature. Darwin thought of something like this too. He imagined that one might have particles that would be passed on through the reproductive cells, but he thought that since they came from all parts of the body they might, while there, receive the impressions produced by diet, climatic dif-ferences, or other aspects of the environment. These "pan-genes," as he called them, would thus stream into the germ cells from all parts of the body, after having picked up new kinds of differences during the lifetime of each individual, and hence would replace in the population those variations that would disappear as heredity was blended in the next gen-eration. It was a very unsatisfactory hypothesis, and there was really not the slightest evidence for it. None of Darwin's own contemporaries seem to have believed in it at all. Lyell repu-diated it, Thomas Henry Huxley repudiated it, Joseph Hooker repudiated it, and if those three men repudiated one of Darwin's ideas, you can be sure that there was no support for it anywhere.

When you hear Darwinism discussed today in different parts of the world, it is important to note that by "Darwinism" some people mean the general theory of evolution, the evidences of which have been amplified a hundredfold or a thousandfold since Darwin's day. Other people mean the theory that natural selection is the process whereby species come to differ. Still others, at least in certain parts of the world, mean Darwin's theory of pangenesis, which allows differences in the environment to produce immediate changes in the heredity of people, plants, and animals. One must be aware that when he reads about Darwinism in Western literature, it may have one of the first two meanings, but practically never the third. However, if one reads about Darwinism in Russian writings, it definitely means pangenesis and not natural selection. Already it is apparent that among the ardent adherents of Darwinism in the world today, there are different sorts of Darwinists: Darwinists who believe in one aspect of Darwinism and those who believe in another. There is virtually no one who believes in *all* the doctrines, theories, and hypotheses that Charles Darwin advanced.

In the 1840's, there appeared in Great Britain a book by an anonymous author, who was later identified as Robert Chambers, editor of the famous *Chambers' Encyclopedia.* In that book, *The Vestiges of Creation,* the evidences for evolution, as enumerated above, were set forth in almost the fullness with which Darwin later discussed them, but were, unfortunately, mixed with fable and a great deal of error. Consequently, sober biologists of the time dismissed the work as of little account; and the general public—which bought it, read it avidly, and discussed it eagerly—was largely misled by the nature of the presentation. I mention this because we should realize that, as far as the evidences for evolution are concerned, this aspect was not original with Darwin. He simply did a much better job of assembling and presenting all the evidences than any one before him had done.

Let us now consider the second aspect of Darwin's work— the theory of natural selection. This, too, was not novel. Maupertuis, on the basis of his studies of heredity, had also developed in the 1750's a theory of evolution that involved natural selection; and you may be sure that the idea was not original with him either. Maupertuis supposed that Nature would seize upon the different combinations of hereditary particles that appeared. Whenever new ones arose by chance, as he supposed must sometimes happen since he was of the opinion that the six-fingered deformity had not always been present in the family he studied, then natural selection, by weeding out those hereditary variations—or mutations as we now call them—that produce monstrosities, and by permitting to live and reproduce those that are capable of reproduction, would lead to the evolution of new types. If segregated in different parts of the world, these types, like the presumed giants in Patagonia and dwarfs in Greenland, might in time become new species. Maupertuis obviously made little distinction between races and species, on the one hand, and simple mutations in the genes within a species, on the other; but we must excuse him for this confusion since later scientists who developed the mutation theory were not aware of such distinctions either.

More likely known to Charles Darwin than the ideas of Maupertuis was the work of his grandfather, Erasmus Darwin, who also developed a theory of natural selection, but to whom Darwin himself refers very little in his own work. Where did Darwin actually get the idea of natural selection?

He says, of course, that it came to him after reading Thomas R. Malthus' famous *Essay on Population*—but this may not be quite true. There has recently appeared an essay of great scholarly importance, written by Loren Eiseley, professor of anthropology at the University of Pennsylvania. Professor Eiseley has unearthed three papers written by a friend, or perhaps only an acquaintance, of Darwin, a man named Edward Blyth. The essays were written, I think, before Darwin knew him, for the first of them actually appeared while he was still on his voyage around the world. In these three essays, Edward Blyth outlines very clearly the theory of natural selection in all its details. We may be quite sure that the journal in which these essays appeared in 1835, '36, and '37 was one that Darwin read dutifully from cover to cover, not only while he was on the voyage but afterward. It seems unthinkable that he could have missed these articles altogether; in fact, there is very good evidence that he did not. In 1842, '44, and '47, Darwin wrote notes and sketches of his theory in preliminary form. In those notes and preliminary abstracts, one finds him using certain odd words such as "inosculate," used not in the sense of kissing but of simple adjoining, and used by Darwin in a particular context, just as Blyth had used exactly the same odd word in exactly the same context. We know, too, that in later years Darwin corresponded with Blyth, who went to India; that he thought very highly of Blyth as a thinker; and that he was particularly interested in his studies of animal variation. Yet never, in note or word or letter, and certainly not in any publication, did Darwin make reference to the three essays by Edward Blyth on natural selection. The internal evidence seems completely convincing that he had read these and, maybe with a photographic memory, had registered what was in them. Why did he then make no reference to them? It may have been because Blyth used the theory of natural selection not to explain how species can arise from pre-existing species, but rather to explain how species remain constant. The action of selection, he thought, would serve to eliminate not only monsters, but all deviants from the norm, all those abnormal types that arise in every population; and so it would make each species hold true to type, stay fit to continue its existence within the given environment. Darwin evidently absorbed Blyth's idea and turned it over in his own mind for a period of years, perhaps until he had completely forgotten where the idea originated. Then, by a brilliant stroke, he turned the theory upside down to say: "Not only will natural selection keep species constant, it will also, if the environment varies, make the species vary to fit new environments." This was Darwin's master stroke, and one cannot say whether or not he ever consciously knew what a debt he owed to Edward Blyth.

Modern views of the nature of the evolutionary process remain based upon Darwin's ideas in many respects. Thus Darwin thought that only the small changes that arise, the minor variations, would be likely to be involved in the change of species. The big ones would produce too great a disharmony in the organism, so that very likely any such deviant would die or be unable to reproduce. After genes were discovered and it became known that they can mutate to assume new forms and to produce new hereditary characteristics, it was at first thought, during the early years of the twentieth century, that rather large changes, such as the ones commonly observed, might be the real basis of evolutionary change. It was even supposed that new species might occasionally come from single new mutations as Maupertuis and, later, Hugo de Vries and Richard Goldschmidt assumed. The more this problem has been studied, however, the more biologists are convinced that in this respect Darwin was essentially correct. It is the little changes that normally form the basis for the adaptation of species to new kinds of environments, while radical changes usually result in death or infertility and become eliminated.

It is mainly our views of heredity that differ from Darwin's, not our views of the effects of natural selection. When one sees clearly that heredity is based upon genes and chromosomes in Mendelian fashion, one quickly sees also that there is no inevitable loss of hereditary variability from the population in each generation. On the contrary, unless specific forces act to modify the frequency of genes in a population, the reproductive processes will simply maintain each gene in the same relative frequency it has previously had. This is a very important genetic principle; we call it the Hardy-Weinberg principle, named for a mathematician and a physician who independently worked it out in 1908. It is always rather amusing to me that Hardy, the mathematician, who spent most of his life working with imaginary numbers, is said to have boasted to the end of his career that nobody could possibly say of him that during his lifework as a mathematician he had ever done anything of the least practical value. But one night a geneticist friend gave him a problem. The problem was: What will happen to the frequency of genes in a population breeding at random? Will certain alternative genes become rarer and others become commoner? Or will they stay in the same proportions? This was a very simple problem for a mathematician. He worked it out and shortly afterward published a little paper in *Nature*. Without Hardy's principle, many problems of the utmost practical importance for human populations the world around would be without a solution. We would not, for example, even begin to be able to calculate what damage is done to the genes of a population by exposure to X-rays and to fall-out.

Other developments in evolutionary genetics have been added to the Darwinian view. We now realize that, in addition to natural selection, there are certain other kinds of factors that change the frequencies of genes in populations. Mutation itself will do this. If of two alternative kinds of genes one mutates more frequently to the other than the reverse, the more mutable gene might mutate itself right out of existence in a period of time, or so one would think, and only the more stable gene would be left. Actually, this doesn't quite happen, but an equilibrium is set up such that the more mutable gene is rarer and the more stable gene is commoner. At any rate, mutation can change the commonness or rarity of hereditary characteristics in a population. Next there is what we call gene flow, the introduction of genes from one population into another. When individuals migrate and thereafter leave some of their genes behind them in the population, this is called gene flow. It, too, may make certain genes commoner and others rarer if there are initial differences between the two populations. Finally, chance itself, at least in very small populations, may change the frequencies of genes.

Yet we are convinced today more than ever that 999 times out of every 1,000 those genes that persist in a population, those genes that are more successful, are those that are preserved by natural selection. In other words, when two different hereditary types enter into reproduction in a population, if one of them has a higher probability of endowing its possessors with the capacity to live to adulthood, or if one of them makes its possessor more fertile than the other, then in the course of time over many generations, the gene that improves viability, the gene that has the higher fertility, will displace the other in the population.

Of course, this fitness is quite relative. It is not necessarily deducible from the appearance of an organism. In Baltimore, flies with wings get along much better in life than flies without wings. They fly from garbage can to garbage can; they find places to mate and to lay their eggs, and they multiply. Wingless flies, which sometimes arise by mutation, are greatly handicapped in such an environment; but on the island of Kerguelen, in the far southern Indian Ocean, where there are no trees but only grasses, and where strong winds sweep the island day after day the year round, not only the flies but all other kinds of insects that have gotten there and survived are forms with little stubby vestiges of wings or no wings at all. The type of mutation that in one environment leads to elimination of a species may be the means of survival of that species in a different environment.

Human heredity offers another example. In our Negro population in the United States, there is an abnormal kind of hemoglobin in the red cells that produces severe anemia when a person inherits it from both parents. It is a very disadvantageous trait, often leading to the death of the person with this so-called sickle-cell hemoglobin. Our Negro population was of course derived from Africa. In Africa there are even more individuals, proportionately, with sickle-cell hemoglobin than there are among Negroes in this country. The reason for this is certainly curious. It has been discovered within the past few years. In many parts of equatorial Africa, tertian human malaria is one of the chief causes of death. In fact, it is thought to have been the greatest killer of mankind throughout history. For some reason the plasmodium, the parasite that causes tertian malaria, does not live well on sickle-cell hemoglobin. It lives upon and likes normal hemoglobin and plump red cells. The difference between sickle-cell hemoglobin and normal hemoglobin is produced by a single gene difference. So in Negro populations three kinds of children are born: those with two doses of the sickle-cell hemoglobin gene, those with two doses of the normal hemoglobin gene, and those with one gene of each sort. Children who have two doses of the sickle-cell hemoglobin gene die of anemia, since their tissues do not get enough oxygen. In Africa, those who have two doses of the normal hemoglobin gene are very often victims of malaria. The only ones who have a really good chance to survive and transmit their genes to the next generation are those with one gene of each sort. Again, we see that a gene that in one environment or in one assortment of genes is harmful may under other circumstances be necessary to reproductive survival. We must therefore think today in terms of a very complex system of interacting factors that determine the outcome of natural selection. We must regard the interplay of genes with one another, the interplay of genes affecting viability with those affecting fertility. Sometimes the gene that promotes fertility may not be a very good gene for the population as a whole because it cuts down on viability. In the long run it is the over-all effect of a gene that will determine its endurance in the population.

When we consider human evolution, we see that since human conditions have changed greatly—perhaps not as much as from the garbage cans of Baltimore to the island of Kerguelen for the flies, but, nevertheless, a great deal—there is no force in the argument that because a certain thing was of value to human survival one hundred thousand years ago, it must be of value to survival now. Sir Arthur Keith, the anthropologist, wrote that war was necessary to human nature, an evil that we must put up with because it was responsible for the development of combativeness and aggressiveness, among the most important human characteristics. Even if this were true, war in primitive times among savage tribes was really only in name the same as today's war between civilized nations, which may be nuclear extermination; and there is no reason at all to equate present situations with those that determined the kind of natural selection to which the human species was exposed 50,000 to 100,000 years ago, or even, for that matter, 5,000 years ago.

It would not be appropriate to conclude this contribution to a symposium on Darwin, Marx, and Wagner without commenting upon Jacques Barzun's analysis in 1937 of Darwin and of Darwinism. Barzun clearly recognized that the acclaim of Darwin was a product of the ideology of the times, the post-romantic period, and also that Darwin was a master synthesizer rather than a great original mind. Like Marx and Wagner, Darwin was indeed a symbol of rising materialistic, mechanistic thought. But Barzun harbored an imperfect idea of the present scientific status of natural selection, which, as I have briefly tried to indicate, stands in a stronger position in the thinking of biologists today than ever before. Barzun affirms that although natural selection obviously exists, it is not creative. On the contrary, biologists have assumed a priori that natural selection is creative and now have evidence that this is so, although until quite recently there was very little experimental study of the process and how it works. In consequence, Barzun emphasizes the mechanistic materialism of Darwinism, which he seems to regard as an inescapable consequence of a belief in natural selection as the primary evolutionary factor. To escape from this, Barzun wishes to assume that evolution is produced by some other kind of factor that is not material and mechanistic. This he thinks he finds in the nature of hereditary variation, that is to say, in mutation itself. Yet I am confident that there is a consensus among geneticists today that if there is anything clearly materialistic and mechanistic in the whole of biological conceptualization, it lies in the nature of the gene, the action of the gene, and the mutation of the gene. Barzun's mistake is one that many have made in the past, viz., the mistake of thinking that there is any escape from a materialistic, mechanistic point of view in natural science. Natural science deals with matter and energy, with phenomena that are material and that work according to probabilistic laws, with phenomena that can be observed, and observed repeatedly. It is a self-consistent scheme of things. As long as you ask a question of natural science, the answer comes back in terms of a self-contained system of thought, mechanistic and materialistic, because that is what science deals with.

This is not to say, however, that all reality is to be reduced to mechanism and materialism. Science may be ignorant of many things that are real. Science is a construct of the human mind, and the human mind itself a product of the evolutionary process. The mind depends upon the existence of certain senses that have an adaptive value and have appeared over the course of time in certain species through the agency of natural selection. And the mind of man itself is a tool which has appeared in the course of evolution, a means whereby man can make successful adjustments to the environment in which he and his ancestors have lived. The mind is, therefore, limited to certain kinds of relationships and perhaps can deal successfully only with those things that we say "make sense"; that is, that are apparent to the senses, are repeatable as observations, are related to matter and energy, and are essentially mechanistic. But it is a blind scientist, in my opinion, who would maintain that because this is all his science can deal with, this is necessarily all that really exists. It would be tantamount to saying that because we don't have radios in our brains, radio waves don't exist. We must recognize, as our great American historian Carl Becker put it, that this structure of science which is revolutionizing our lives is itself a human construct, a product of the evolutionary process.

We must recognize, too, that as such it is less a picture of total reality than it is "man's supreme product of ingenuity, his most magnificent work of art." If we look at things in these terms, I believe we need see no ultimate conflict between the scientific way of looking at nature and the attitudes that have prevailed in the humanities. But we must recognize the limitations of science in dealing with values as well as the powers of science in dealing with material things.

Richard Hofstadter

Darwinism and Western Thought

HENRY ADAMS, who, like some of his contemporaries, at times confused the idea of evolution with the idea of progress, once suggested that he had a simple disproof of evolution—just a look at the history of the American Presidency from Washington to Grant. We are less likely than Adams' generation to be optimistic about progress, more likely to agree with his pessimism. Someone has appropriately remarked that whereas a hundred years ago we worried about the survival of the fittest, we now worry about the survival of anyone. In some ways it is this grim predicament that causes us to look back with curiosity to see what has been made of evolution in social thinking. I think I should warn you before I get into the substance of my lecture that it marches off in two different directions. The first half of it is devoted to telling what Darwin's generation and the generation that immediately followed him made of his ideas in social theory and why we have good reason to think that they were almost entirely wrong on almost all counts. The second half will attempt to suggest to you that we should not overstress the business of blaming their failures for our present problems.

At any rate, very soon after the publication of *Origin of Species* in 1859, Darwinism acquired such an importance in the intellectual world that every serious thinker felt obliged to reckon with its implications, and such prestige that every ideologist wanted to claim it and make use of it to strengthen his pre-existing ideas. The social thinkers of the late nineteenth century had a powerful impulse to unify knowledge. Their thought was usually aimed at synthesis, at the formation of a grand system in which all knowledge would be comprehended. As early as 1848, Comte declared in his first sentence of *A General View of Positivism* that ". . . the object of all true philosophy is to frame a system which shall comprehend human life under every aspect, social as well as individual." This drive toward synthesis thus predated Darwin's work, but it was strengthened by the sweeping implications of evolutionism. To a significant degree, therefore, social speculation, and what one might call a certain kind of intellectual propaganda, between 1859 and the end of the century, took its course along a path which, it was believed, would finally lead to a completed system of thought in which society would be understood as a segment of nature and social evolution would be understood as an extension of biological evolution. I need hardly make a secret at the outset of my conviction that this path proved in the end to be a blind alley. Many of the social Darwinian thinkers of the late nineteenth century lived long enough to see their hopes disappointed. Their efforts at synthesis were abandoned if not repudiated by their successors. We have ceased in most cases to study them. We no longer honor them. Of course, we enjoy the luxury of hindsight over this episode in modern thought, and we have the great advantage over its contemporaries of knowing, or thinking we know, where it led; but we ought not to be too condescending to the thinkers of the last half of the nineteenth century who felt it necessary to explore the social Darwinian path. The great insights of Darwin had been set before them in all their grandeur and promise. It would have been strange if these thinkers had not been tempted to extract from such insights every possible bit of illumination for the social as well as the natural world. Believing as they did in the unity of knowledge, it would have been remarkable if they had not tried to build upon the most striking idea of contemporary science a unified system of thought.

The thinkers of the late nineteenth century, like thinkers of other eras, were engaged not simply in the pursuit of truth but also in a contest over social and political ideals. The French Revolution had shattered the pattern of the older Europe. The development of industrialism, democracy, and nationalism had given rise to a variety of new competing interests and ideas. The middle classes were asserting themselves against the spokesmen of the old order, and behind the middle classes—peering, as it were, ominously over their shoulders—were aggressive new spokesmen of the proletariat.

While some men from the older nations were establishing the authority and carrying the trade of Europe to far corners of the globe, other men were creating new nations on the European Continent. In 1831, when Darwin was waiting in Plymouth to set out on the momentous voyage of the "Beagle," Parliament was agitated over the Reform Bill, and mob violence broke out in Bristol. During the next few years, while Darwin was sailing around the world, Parliament was trying to cope with the realities of industrialism by passing a new factory act and a new Poor Law. While Darwin was at work on *The Structure and Distribution of Coral Reefs*, which appeared in 1842, England was being rocked by the Chartists' agitations. In 1848, when he had among his papers a completed but unpublished first sketch of the theory of natural selection and was working on the first volume of his *Cirripedia*, the Continent was shaken by the liberal revolution,

and Marx and Engels published the *Communist Manifesto*.
The year 1859, when *Origin of Species* was published, was
also the year of Marx's *Critique of Political Economy*, whose
preface brilliantly spelled out the materialist interpretation
of history and Marx's own scheme of social evolution. It was
also the year of Samuel Smiles's *Self-Help*, a sacred text of
competitive capitalism, and of John Stuart Mill's *Essay on
Liberty*. In 1871, the year of *The Descent of Man*, the Franco-
Prussian War ended, and the German Empire was established. In 1882, the year of Darwin's death, the British Fleet
bombarded Alexandria. By that time the nations of Europe
had gone far on their way toward the partition of the remaining uncolonized portions of the world.

Darwinism appeared, then, at a time when conservatives
were looking for fresh and more authoritative answers to the
challenge of democracy and liberalism, when spokesmen of
private capitalism were trying to resist the encroachments of
the national state, when prophets of nationalism were seeking justifications for national strife, and when imperialists
were advocating and justifying expansion. The ideas of evolution and natural selection could thus never develop in a social vacuum but had to be absorbed into Western thought in
the midst of arguments over competition and collectivism,
laissez faire and state control, democracy and liberty, nationalism and imperialism.

A brief reminder of the main elements in Darwin's theory
of natural selection will help us to see how each of these elements was translated into social terms. First, Darwin postu-
lated, as Malthus and Spencer had done before him, that
within each species more organisms are constantly generated
than can be nourished and supported by their environment.
Second, because of the rapid rate at which living forms increase, there takes place a constant struggle for existence, a

constant competition for food and other means of survival.
Third, some variation of physical type always occurs within
a species. Not all organisms are equally equipped for survival. Those whose variations are better adapted to the environment in which they must live are the ones that survive
and reproduce themselves. Fourth, the offspring of these
survivors inherit their favorable variations. Finally, the accumulation of such small favorable variations over a very
long period of time results in the emergence of new species.

Now the key terms in this scheme of thought are "struggle," "survival," "variation," "inheritance," "adaptation,"
and "environment." When the ideologues of social Darwinism set to work on this scheme, they tried to translate Darwin's main categories into social categories. The struggle for
existence became economic competition or, perhaps, war.
Survival became economic success or military predomi-
nance. The Darwinian emphasis on the inheritance of variations of unequal value in survival was taken as further evidence of the social value of human inequality, whether it
be inequality between individuals or between races. Adaptation to environment was elevated to a social as well as a biological value. To adapt was to be superior, and since one
adapts, sociologically, to a society, many thinkers identified
society with the environment. The whole scheme of development was taken by many thinkers to be a promising analogue
of social progress, and many concluded that the mechanisms
of natural selection were the chief, or even the only,
mechanisms of human progress. Even the conception of
geological periods of time, which Darwin believed necessary to bring about new species, was appropriated by some
social philosophers. Long periods of time would be necessary
to bring about social change, they argued, just as it took eons
for the species to develop into the multiple varieties on the

earth and to produce the highest forms of animal life. Therefore, all schemes for hasty social reform flew in the face of
nature.

The trouble was not that it was difficult to construct such
analogies between nature and society but that it was all too
easy. The thinkers of the last four decades of the nineteenth
century flung themselves into a Darwinian free-for-all. But
the more speculative elaborations of social evolution (as
they called it) they were able to conceive, the clearer it became that the precise implications of Darwinism for society
were not a matter upon which men could readily agree. It
was easy, for instance, to see the life of men in society as a
constant struggle, but it was not so easy to interpret the meaning of the struggle. Which, in fact, were the struggling units?
Individual men, groups, business firms, tribes or races, na-
tion-states? It made a great deal of difference how this question was answered. A social theory built upon the struggle of
individuals would in practice point to one direction. A social theory based upon a struggle of groups might point to
opposite conclusions. The struggle of individuals seemed
analogous at many points to economic competition. That of
tribes or races seemed analogous to war; but, many writers
argued, if war is the true equivalent of the struggle for
existence in nature, then solidarity among the individuals in
the warring tribes or nations is necessary for the survival
of the group. Yet if solidarity within a society is the important element in survival, how could one sanction the principle of struggle among individuals that would destroy solidarity? Understandably, a whole generation was thrown into
confusion by such problems. Some thinkers, notably Herbert
Spencer, compounded the confusion by trying to have it both
ways. In his individualist mood he was all for competition
and the devil take the hindmost. At the same time he ad-

hered to an organismic theory of the state which hardly seemed consistent with his individualism. Karl Marx and his followers complicated matters by arguing that the real struggle was one between classes. Marx thought that, as he expressed it, Darwin gave him a basis in natural science for the class struggle in history. Later social scientists concluded that the important struggle to take account of was not among individuals or nations but among institutions, habits, and types of character. But this takes us a long way from Darwin.

Even the ideal of a science of society was affected in an ironic way. The attempt to translate natural selection into social terms, oddly enough, did not lead to an era of "social science." That is to say, it did not bring about the kind of careful, fact-minded observation, classification, and laborious study and elaborate notation of endless minute details that we associate with the work of Darwin and the other great naturalists of his era. Darwin gave the world a theoretical scheme which, though revolutionary, was essentially simple; he pulled a light freight of ideas with a powerful engine of fact. He permitted himself a few major theoretical suggestions. The social Darwinian thinkers launched upon an orgy of speculation. Darwin accumulated an elaborate mass of data; his followers usually worked with occasional illustrations, partial clues, and fragmentary observations. He practiced science; they were so devoted to preaching it that they had little time for its practice. Perhaps there is a clue in this to the character of much positivistic thinking. To revere science is not to be scientific. In fact, reverence sometimes gets in the way of science.

Two basic and mutually antagonistic views and uses, I have suggested, were made of Darwinism. First, Darwinism was used in the service of conservatism, industrial capitalism, and laissez faire. This kind of thinking, propagated by

Herbert Spencer in England and by William Graham Sumner in the United States, was largely an Anglo-American phenomenon. The development of the Continental economies
was such that laissez faire never had such popularity. At any
rate, social Darwinism flourished from the 1860's until about
the end of the century, when it ceased to be fashionable at
the level of serious thinking and passed into the limbo of
stale popular clichés. In the 1880's, William Graham Sumner was writing a passage like this: "The millionaires are a
product of natural selection, acting on the whole body of men
to pick out those who can meet the requirement of certain
work to be done. It is because they are thus selected that
wealth, both their own and that entrusted to them, aggre-
gates under their hands. They may fairly be regarded as the
naturally selected agents of society for certain work." I
have other such passages but I will spare you. At the time
Sumner wrote these lines, what he said was still acceptable to
many thinkers as serious social thought, but a whole generation of intellectual critics and of social reformers ham-
mered away at these notions until the hopeless simplicity as
well as the smugness of such utterances became all too evident to reflective men. It is of course true that the high-brow
sociology of one generation may become the low-brow sociology of the next. When Robert and Helen Lynd made their
second famous investigation of Middletown in the 1930's,
they found that individualist social Darwinism had survived
as folklore. "You can't make the world all planned and soft,"
they were told by a Middletown businessman. "The strongest and best survive—that's the law of nature after all—
always has been and always will be." I hasten to say that I
realize that some serious thinkers still advocate thoroughgo-
ing laissez faire. I have not forgotten the ideas of Hayek, von
Mises, Henry Simon, Milton Friedman, and others who are

contemporaries. But such exponents of laissez faire today are the best proof of the obsoleteness of the social Darwinian arguments, for these men disdain to use such arguments. They, too, recognize almost as fully as any advocate of the welfare state that the synthetic philosophies of the social-Darwinian era have not held up. Even Herbert Spencer, the precursor and archangel of the social Darwinian revelation, had sadly admitted it near the close of his lifetime. In his *Principles of Ethics*, published in 1893, he wrote: "The doctrine of evolution has not furnished guidance to the extent I had hoped. Most of the conclusions, drawn empirically, are such as right feelings, enlightened by cultivated intelligence, have already sufficed to establish."

The second phase of social Darwinism was the racist-military phase. This was the main form in which Darwinism was made into a social doctrine on the Continent, though it had influential Anglo-American spokesmen as well. In the years after 1870, as nationalism in Europe passed from an urge toward political and cultural liberation to a climate of mutual hatred, fear, and frustration, and as the imperial colonization of the world once again accelerated, the Darwinian vision of the warfare of nature seemed to become increasingly germane to the contemporary world. Army and navy officers, spokesmen of nationalism and imperialism, could easily refurbish and strengthen their old arguments with new Darwinian metaphors. A new literature of group struggle arose. The argument for national or racial superiority, already widely believed, now seemed to have a natural sanction.

Perhaps, the first of the imperial Darwinians was the English economist, Walter Bagehot, who discussed the pattern of national progress in his *Physics and Politics* in 1872, in which he observed that those nations which are strongest tend to prevail and in certain marked peculiarities the strongest are the best. The historian J. A. Froude saw the victory of Protestant England over Catholic Spain and the domination of England over Ireland as exemplifications of the principle and concluded that the superior part has a natural right to govern; the inferior part has a right to be governed. Nicholas Danilevsky, a Russian pan-Slavist, who later wrote a critical book on Darwinism, found that each group of people or race is like a species. It seems hardly necessary to add that he found the Slavs the superior race.

Social Darwinian interpretations became prominent after the Franco-Prussian War among both victor and vanquished. Even Ernest Renan referred to war in 1871 as "one of the conditions of progress, the cut of the whip which prevents a country from going to sleep."

Ludwig Gumplowicz, a Polish professor of law, began to elaborate a sociological theory based upon a series of unremitting struggles between racial groups, national states, and social classes. Gustav Ratzenhofer, an Austrian field marshal, elaborated a theory of society based upon self-assertion and the mutual hostility of all men. This hostility, he argued, could be submerged only in war or great projects of co-operative labor. Culture and commerce weaken the social structure but struggle and war consolidate it. "War," wrote the victorious Marshal von Moltke, "is an element of the order of the world established by God. Without war the world would stagnate and lose itself in materialism."

In the United States, John Fiske, James K. Hosmer, Albert J. Beveridge, and Josiah Strong predicted the worldwide supremacy of the Anglo-Saxon peoples. John W. Burgess declared that the Teutonic nations were best fitted to exercise the political leadership of the world. Brooks Adams warned that the nations were engaged in a war to the death.

And Theodore Roosevelt predicted that if the American people ceased to live the strenuous life and lost what he called the great fighting masterful virtues, "then the bolder and stronger peoples will pass us by and win for themselves the domination of the world." And so it went.

The cruder uses of Darwinism by individualists, racists, and nationalists were hardly unchallenged. Time does not permit the full recounting of the successive poundings to which these notions were subjected from 1870 onward. Having attempted this task for our own climate of opinion in my book on *Social Darwinism in American Thought,* I can testify that tracing the decline of these ideas leads one over a long and tortuous path of argumentation. It may be enough now to say that the counterattack came from a great many sources —reformers; Socialists, Christian and Marxian; anti-imperialists—and was urged from a variety of intellectual perspectives. Lester Frank Ward and his followers in American sociology, British Fabians, economists like Thorstein Veblen, the pragmatic school in American philosophy, exponents of national economics and the welfare state in all countries, Continental writers like Prince Peter Kropotkin and Jacques Novicow—all these added their blows. Over the years these opponents of social Darwinism picked away at it so tellingly that we need hardly wonder at its decline. They pointed out —among them T. H. Huxley—that the fundamental terms of the analogy made no sense, because the struggle that takes place among men in society is not exactly a struggle for existence. In natural selection, less fit organisms do not procreate because they do not survive to maturity. In society, as the eugenists began soon enough gloomily to warn, the so-called unfit classes do survive long enough to procreate and in greater numbers than the so-called fit, and there arose a whole school of thought based upon anxiety over the failure of Vassar girls to have more than 1.6 children per person. But the whole use of biological definitions of fitness in a social setting was soon singled out as preposterous. Perhaps someone was struck by the irony that dyspeptic, neurotic, and even suicidal intellectuals should be preaching the survival of the strong and the hardy.

Once it was accepted that physical characteristics were meaningless for social survival, it became clear that a whole new set of social criteria must be employed. When men began to consider new criteria, the door was open to a reconsideration of the meaningfulness of "nature red in tooth and claw" for social behavior, and to the suggestion—as Lester Ward did suggest—that fitness to survive is something different from real superiority. Ward also stressed the inefficiency of nature in the raw as compared with human techniques of plant and animal culture. It was easy to show that nature was wasteful of organisms, that it brought millions into existence while only hundreds survived, and that human intelligence moved even toward biological goals, not to speak of social ones, in a more direct and economical way. Once it was possible to see that artificial processes are actually superior to natural ones, it was also possible to abandon the absurd worship of nature upon which the mystique of social Darwinism rested. Other critics, like John Fiske in the United States and Henry Drummond in Great Britain, stressed the survival value in human affairs of the non-ferocious qualities, of altruism and love, especially as manifested in the human family, and in this they had a predecessor in Darwin.

But the most satisfactory general critique of social Darwinism, in my opinion, was made by the American pragmatists, who themselves started from a Darwinian standpoint in the sense that they were concerned among other things with

the role of mind in survival. The social Darwinians had originated the idea that "society equals environment"; that is to
say, what the natural environment is to plants and animals,
society is to the human species. When one considers animal
life there is little use in questioning the environment as a
whole. True, animals modify their environment in small
ways—beavers, for instance—and within limits change it
when they migrate. But in the subhuman world of nature, the
environment is an absolute; it is there, and the creature must
adapt. What the pragmatists realized most effectively is that
the moment human consciousness appears on the scene, with
its capacity for formulating goals and manipulating both
the natural and the social environment, the whole game is
played differently. Mind, consciousness, is not merely pas-
sive or adaptive. When mind begins to change environment,
the conditions of biological evolution are not only super-
seded, they are in a sense reversed. As William James put it:

> The knower is an actor, and a coefficient of the truth on one
> side, whilst on the other he registers the truth which he helps
> to create. Mental interests, hypotheses, postulates, so far as
> they are bases for human action—action which to a great
> extent transforms the world—help to *make* the truth which
> they declare. In other words, there belongs to mind, from its
> birth upward, a spontaneity, a vote. It is in the game and
> not a mere looker-on, and its judgments of the *should be*,
> its ideals, cannot be peeled off from the body of the cogi-
> tandum as if they were excrescences, or meant, at most,
> survival.

So when human consciousness operates, survival ceases to
be the all-pervasive and controlling goal of existence and becomes instead merely an assumption upon which may be
based the formulation of other more complex, more interesting, more human, and more humane goals. The crude, mo-

nistic, positivistic assumption of a continuity of principle between nature and society is thus ruined, and we are free to
erect such understanding of society as we are capable of
achieving, on independent sociological and historical principles. Biology as a foundation for sociology is in the dust bin;
we are free to realize, even though our academic psychology
has been slow to realize it, that biology will not even take us
very far as a foundation for psychology.

Within thirty years of *The Descent of Man* it was hardly
possible for a serious and informed thinker to adhere to the
old hope of a monistic synthesis of all the sciences. Now it
was the qualitative differences between the operative principles of society and those of nature that were taking the fore-
ground.

Most of us, then, think of social Darwinism as a more or
less closed episode in intellectual history, but there is less
agreement about its meaning. There are two widespread
and intimately related theses on the subject from which I
should like to enter a dissent. I propose to call them the
intellectualist fallacy and the obscurantist fallacy. Those
who commit the intellectualist fallacy assume—and indeed
at times seem flatly to assert—that we are ruled by ideas and
by little else. Placing this heavy burden of responsibility
upon ideas, they say that the whole worship of force, so
prominent in Europe between 1870 and 1914, should be laid
at the door of the Darwinian, positivistic, mechanistic complex of ideas; and there was a time, indeed, about fifteen
years ago when these ideas by extension were even made responsible in very great part for the evils of the two world
wars of the twentieth century and of totalitarianism. The effect of the intellectualist fallacy is to overplay the influence
of such ideas by stripping them out of the social context in
which they were formed and interpreted. The effect of the

obscurantist fallacy is to suggest that the bad influence of the social Darwinian ideas is attributable to the fact that they were naturalistic ideas. They undermine social morality, it is held, because they undermine religious and supernatural sanctions for behavior, leaving no canons but those of nature red in tooth and claw. We can see the intellectualist fallacy in operation when the publishers of the revised 1958 edition of Jacques Barzun's *Darwin, Marx, Wagner* tell us on the jacket that the triumphs of the late nineteenth-century age of materialism "have according to Professor Barzun been *the source* of the 20th century's characteristic problems." Professor Barzun himself is much more careful. In fact, he tells us only that the ideas and methods of materialistic mechanism have been *a* source of real woe in our day. However, his discussion of the issue is such as to make his editors' view of his analysis a reasonable one, and it is certainly one that is commonly made. (I feel a little sensitive about the intellectualist fallacy because, although I don't think I committed it in so many words in my book on social Darwinism, I believe the effect of the book was perhaps to encourage it.) Another writer, John Hallowell, tells us that positivism, by which he means what I mean by social Darwinism, was as important as any other single factor in the decline of liberalism and the victory of fascism. Other writers compound the intellectualist fallacy with a note of obscurantism. "It was boys schooled by the generation of materialism," Carleton J. H. Hayes tells us at the close of his book on *A Generation of Materialism, 1871 to 1900*, "who would grow up to fight the World War and it was some of their sons who would follow supermen into the totalitarian state and into totalitarian war." If this were simply a statement about a chronological sequence of generations, it would be too obvious to be made. But it suggests that the materialist ideas of the generation of material-

ism were a distinct and special source of what the sons and
grandsons of that generation endured. Yet I wonder if it
would not be just as fair, and just as unfair, if in a book,
say, on the generation from 1520 to 1550, to assert that its
members were drunk on religious and theological dispute
and that the persecutions of the late sixteenth century and
the horrors of the Thirty Years War must be attributed to
the theology of the Reformation. Surely, the victims of the
St. Bartholomew's Day massacre and the religious wars could
not have found their fate any more pleasant because it was
brought on by religious differences rather than by a naturalistic philosophy of struggle. Western man, with centuries of
religious militancy and persecution behind him, did not
need to stumble on a materialist philosophy to provide him
for the first time with a rationale for violence or exploitation. Given the impulse to exploit or persecute, both materialist and non-materialist philosophies can be bent to
serve the purpose.

I hope I may succeed in being clear about where the difference of opinion lies. I share the dislike of these writers
whom I have quoted for the positivist mentality of the late
nineteenth century. I agree that ideas do have effects in history, and I hasten to agree that the crude social Darwinian
image of nature as a battlefield and of struggle as the only
source of progress had bad effects in so far as it had any
effect. I agree, finally, that this experience ought to warn
us against simple monistic, mechanistic philosophies and
against crude attempts to transfer scientific findings to social
thought. My differences hang on these points: First, I object
to the implicit assumption which is often made, though few
writers seem to care explicitly to defend it, that ideas not
merely influence but actually control history. I particularly
object to this when it is assumed that influential social ideas

develop solely or largely out of their own internal dynamic, more or less unaffected by the demands and the canons of the society from which they emerge. I insist that ideas, though they have consequences, must also be thought of as *being* consequences themselves. Otherwise, we may be in danger of reducing our inquiries into the problems of our time to an exercise in the history of ideas and thus of distracting ourselves from a necessary work of social criticism, for it is institutions as well as ideas that we must scrutinize.

Second, the cruder and more violent philosophies that grew up around Darwinism were not logically inevitable extensions of Darwin's theory or of naturalism, but became dominant notions in some circles because they suited some men's purposes. Alternative uses of the social significance of Darwinism were available to them, and I propose simply that these alternatives, when they were rejected, were rejected not because of any intrinsic inferiority or lack of substance but rather because they were less suited to the needs of certain social interests.

Finally, as one with a naturalist and secularist turn of mind, I object to the imputation that the ill uses that were often made of Darwinism in social thought could be made simply because Darwinism gave rise to naturalistic and secularist views. I reject the inference that there is a logically necessary connection between naturalistic thinking and the immense social mischief of our time. Philosophies of struggle, violence, ruthless competition, and racism existed long before natural selection was formulated by Darwin. No one, I believe, cares to deny this, or to assert that Darwinism originated such views. But we must go back and look at some of the crassest assertions of these views in pre-Darwinian days to remind ourselves how forceful, how raw and "Darwinian" they were, in the absence of Darwin. Carlyle may

serve as a good case in point, for without benefit of any
clues to natural selection, he was preaching, before 1859,
all the worst implications of what we call social Darwinism.
When he wrote, "Man is created to fight; he is perhaps best
of all definable as a born soldier, his life a battle and a
march under the right general," he was drawing upon religious as much as natural imagery; and when he wrote concerning the Opium War, "Our friends of China who guiltily
refused to trade, had we not to argue with them in cannon
shot at last and convince them that they ought to trade?", he
was drawing all the practical conclusions of the imperial
Darwinists well in advance of their work. "After all," wrote
Thomas Hughes in *Tom Brown's School Days,* which was
published the year before *The Origin of Species,* "what
would life be without fighting? From the cradle to the grave
fighting, rightly understood, is the business, the real highest,
honestest business, of every son of man. It is no good for
Quakers or any other body of men to uplift their voices
against fighting; human nature is too strong for them; I am
dead against crying peace when there is no peace." It was
Charles Kingsley, the apostle of muscular Christianity and
not of muscular Darwinism, who wrote: "You Malays and
Dyaks of the Sarawak, you are the enemies of Christ the
prince of peace, you are beasts, all the more dangerous because you have a semi-human cunning. I will, like David,
hate you with a perfect hatred even as though you were my
enemies. I will blast you out with grape and rockets, I will
beat you as small as the dust before the wind." What need
did such fellows have of the gods of natural selection when
they had the God of the Old Testament?

    To realize how antihumane racism could be before Dar-
winian racism was possible, we need only contemplate the
ugly brutality of Carlyle's *Occasional Discourse on the Nig-*

ger Question, written in 1849. Indeed, some of the coarsest formulations of racism were given us well before 1859, in America, by apologists for slavery, most of whom invoked Biblical texts and religious sanctions at a time when naturalistic sanctions were less authoritative.

But it will be said that the point is not that Darwinism originated such views or that they could not have existed without it, but simply that Darwinism strengthened them. And I have no desire to deny that Darwinism was used to strengthen them and give them a kind of philosophical form. But before Darwinism and poor Darwin are made to carry too heavy a freight of responsibility, we should ask *why* it was so used. Was it because the social Darwinian interpretations of natural selection were correct and intellectually irresistible, or was it because nineteenth-century society was so constituted that some of its spokesmen found a convenient way of manhandling and stretching Darwin's ideas to suit various purposes we cannot condone? Did people get out of Darwin an added and specious authority for things they were already doing and preaching; or did they begin to do and preach because Darwin, as it were, put them up to it? We should not permit ourselves to forget that people made out of Darwin what they did because they already were what they were when he came along.

I am constrained to argue the case that Darwinism was intrinsically a neutral instrument, capable of being used by both sides in a moral and social debate. Interpretations of Darwinism alternative to those of the ruthless school were offered, and I think it would be conceding too much to the social Darwinians to say that their arguments were superior to those of their opponents and critics. I trust I have given some reasons for my own view that they were in fact inferior. The onus for the unhappy uses of Darwinism should not, I think, rest primarily on Darwin or Darwinism or naturalism, but should be shared, and shared in much the greater part, by that raw, exploitive, aggressive, industrial society that both gave birth to Darwinism and molded social Darwinism in its own image.

We can test the assumption that the uses of Darwinism were decided more by the social environment in which it was interpreted than by its own internal logic by asking two questions. Was Darwinism interpreted differently in different environments? Was it interpreted differently by men in the same environment, but of different interests and preconceptions? Of course it was. In the Anglo-American world, individualist Darwinism became an intellectual force. On the Continent it never had much effect. Karl Marx, presuming to speak for the proletariat, saw Darwinism shedding one kind of light on industrialism. Spencer, looking at it from the standpoint of a middle-class English dissenter, saw another. Kropotkin, the left-wing anarchist, saw in it lessons almost directly antithetical to those drawn by William Graham Sumner, the right-wing anarchist. One evolutionist, Sir Arthur Keith, said that, much as he disliked war, he could conceive of no substitute that would serve so well for what he called "the race health of humanity" and the building of stronger races. But another biologist, David Starr Jordan, found that war is dysgenic because it draws the healthiest young men into armies and kills them off. The militarist and race-struggle school concluded that conflict and war were eternal laws of progress. Bagehot and Spencer agreed that they had fostered progress in earlier periods of history, but that this was no longer true. Others said that it had never been true. Spencer and Lester Ward, who agreed on almost nothing else, felt that optmistic conclusions could not be drawn from evolution unless one believed in the inheritance of acquired characteristics. Others said that progress went on even without such inheritance. Still other Darwinians, like Sumner, offered little hope for progress in any case.

Darwinism has been charged with responsibility for racism and, by extension, for much of nazi ideology. But Darwinism, from the very beginning, could have been interpreted, and indeed by some was interpreted, in just the opposite way. As Gertude Himmelfarb points out in her recent book *Darwin and the Darwinian Revolution*, Darwinism, appearing at the climax of the debate over Negro slavery in the American Civil War was first enlisted in that argument. The only difficulty, she observes, was that Darwin's ideas could be made to favor either side. The most obvious deduction was the antiracists' one, she thinks. The theory of evolution, by denying the separateness of varieties in species, also denied the separateness and thus the intrinsic inferiority of some races. When Asa Gray, the American naturalist, first read *Origin of Species*, he blanched at being made kin to the Hottentot. Some racists opposed the book because they couldn't bear the implication that the various races of man came from a common stock. Darwin himself believed that there are higher and lower races, and did not flinch from the conclusion that many of the lower races would, as he said, be eliminated. But just to keep the matter as complicated as in historical fact it was, Darwin was an ardent abolitionist, and abolition was indeed the only social issue of his time to which he paid any attention. As to fascist racism, there would be no point in saying that it did not take cues from Darwinism or from the positivist climate of ideas, since it took cues from everything. But its racism can hardly be laid at the door of an excessive piety for science, for scientifically, nazi racism was a pure anachronism. It was formulated after there was hardly a naturalist or ethnologist left

alive in the world who still believed in racial superiority
and inferiority.

The formulation, indeed, of fascist ideology is a perfect
proof case of the way in which the milieu shapes the ideas.
In 1863, one could have argued with at least some show of
plausibility that racism was a likely deduction from Darwinism. To hold the same in 1933 was preposterous. Yet
probably more than any other thing it is the experience of
totalitarianism that has colored our view during the last
twenty years of the social Darwinian epoch, for in its racism
and its emphasis on violence and struggle, fascism appears
to have overtones of social Darwinism. We thought we heard
familiar voices out of an earlier era when Mussolini told
us: "Strife is the origin of all things; strife will always remain at the root of human nature like a supreme fatality."
Or when Hitler told us: ". . . The stronger has to rule; only
the born weakling can consider this as cruel. The fight for
daily bread makes all those succumb who are weak, sickly,
and less determined." Of course, there is a good deal of social Darwinism in this, but I have also seen totalitarian
thought traced not only to social Darwinism and positivism
but to Hegelianism and German Idealism generally, to pragmatism, romanticism, traditionalism, and irrationalism. The
trouble with these efforts at reconstructing intellectual gen-
ealogy is that they are all entirely misleading precisely because they are all partially correct. Styles of thought that
are so eclectic and have as many filiations as fascism can
also be said to have no filiations. It will not do to single
out of the whole disordered fascist mélange those aspects
which have to do with social Darwinism alone.

We have come, perhaps a bit abruptly, to the end, and I
must summarize what I believe to be a defensible perspective
on the social applications of Darwinism. I think the whole

attempt to apply Darwinian theories to social affairs was a
mistake, that it was a mistake quite aside from any reservations that we might have about the adequacy of natural selection as an attempt to account for development. I believe
the attempt failed not because it was done in the wrong
way, but because the task was impossible in the first place.
The principles and terms governing the natural world are
not those that govern the life of man in society. I believe that
man acquires knowledge of the ways of nature, not to follow them or subordinate himself to them, but to manipulate
them and, in a sense, to surmount them. Natural science may
help us in innumerable ways, but it cannot generate for us
an adequate ethic or an adequate scheme of sociology, economics, or history. Moreover, I consider the search for abso-
lutely universal principles or rules, or terms, by which our
knowledge of nature and our theories of society can be
wrought into some kind of comprehensive interlocking unity,
fruitless. To achieve the unity of knowledge is not merely
a chimerical goal in itself but one which, if taken seriously,
may impede the pursuit of that partial knowledge in which
it is always possible for us to engage fruitfully. At the same
time, I cannot agree with some modern interpreters in laying
an excessively heavy burden of responsibility for our ills
upon the men who made this mistake in the closing decades
of the nineteenth century. Still less can I accept the conclusion that since nineteenth-century positivism was wrong, we
can become right by swinging to the opposite extreme and
insisting that all naturalistic views of the world are inconsistent with the formulation of a humane and acceptable
ethic. For if we recognize that the findings of science cannot
in any case yield us an ethic, we may also recognize that
the limitations and failures of science will not deprive us of
an ethic, much less deprive us of our morals. Our good

behavior, so far as we can control it, rests not upon infer-
ences from science but upon the humane and rational interpretation of the world about us, to which science can con-
tribute only in a humble and marginal way. It will be objected
that to invoke such vague and fallible guides as humanity
and rationality does not promise us conclusiveness or finality.
And this is true; but it is precisely as a warning against the
effort to be conclusive and final that the whole experience
of the social Darwinian generation stands.

Chauncey D. Leake

A Century of Confusion

POINT OF DEPARTURE

TIME REMAINS for us in continual gestation for the birth of the present and the ever coming tomorrows. Any examination of the gestational period yields an exciting story, which is simply the meaning of the word "history." But it is with the obstetrical climax of delivery that we are usually concerned. What is Time delivering? Is the currency of events associated with monsters, angels, or merely more of the usual run of us? Only occasionally do we take a moment to consider the factors influencing our immediate intellectual gestation. When we do, the insights we gain may really be helpful to us.

Our immediate intellectual past is one of confusion, revolution, and counterrevolution, running through the decades since 1859, and so brilliantly spotlighted by Jacques Barzun, the erudite, witty, and urbane Parisian pundit. He has raised a challenging thesis of revolution in science, in political and social economy, and in art, centering around the neurotic trio of Charles Robert Darwin (1809–82) of Shrewsbury, Karl Heinrich Marx (1818–83) of Trèves, and Wilhelm Richard Wagner (1813–83) of Leipzig.

According to Barzun, it was Darwin's book, misnamed *Origin of Species*, published November 24, 1859, that triggered the biological and thus the scientific explosion which

is causing us such concern. It was Marx's formula of prediction for economics, published early in 1859 under the
title *Critique of Political Economy*, that opened our social
and economic revolution to the dismay of many haves and
to the joy of many have-nots. It was Wagner's completion in
1859 of his romantic music drama of love and betrayal,
Tristan and Isolde, that started a confusing series of dramatic activities so disturbing to our stereotyped aesthetic
equanimity.

With respect to the specific year 1859, over one hundred
years ago, the greatest single impact on Western culture was
made by Darwin's treatise. The effort by Marx was scarcely
noted. *Tristan and Isolde* was not accepted for production
until 1862, in Vienna, when it was abandoned after seventy-
seven rehearsals because of the inadequacy of the tenor. It
was finally produced in Munich in 1865.

The immediate reaction to Darwin's book was sharp and
highly controversial. This led to a gradual accumulation of
sound and verifiable data concerning both the origin of, and
the factors involved in, the survival of the various species of
living things, so that the general scientific principle developed by Darwin has become a fixed part of our culture, in
spite of laws still extent in Tennessee. On the other hand, the
controversy aroused by Marx continues. In contrast, the aesthetic confusion opened by Wagner swelled to enormous proportions, engulfing all aspects of social endeavor, and left
Wagner himself stranded decades ago in almost historical
obscurity.

The year 1859 may also be used to mark the end of intellectual romanticism, for it was then that Alexander von
Humboldt died. He exemplified the ideal romantic—a brilliant writer, a great explorer, a wise statesman, and a keen
naturalist, with contributions in astronomy, botany, cartog-

raphy, chemistry, geography, geology, oceanography, and zoölogy. The world became too complex after 1859 for a single genius like him ever to encompass it again.

In the United States, the year 1859 was notable chiefly for the great Lincoln-Douglas debates on slavery, with anxious overtones in economics and politics. With the ominous rifle cracks at Harper's Ferry, the frightful Civil War was on the way. "John Brown's Body" was a marching song, and with inspired words became a battle hymn and a stirring epic by Stephen Vincent Benét. Neither science nor art was esteemed in what was called the "land of the free." Darwin upset our cherished religious beliefs; Marx disturbed our comfortable economic creed; and Wagner set a flamboyant hero-worshiping pageantry pattern of insecurity, exploited to our disgust by Ku Kluxers and to our confusion by Mussolini's Black Shirts and Hitler's Nazis.

COUNTERPOINT

Against the conventional point of view of current Western culture with regard to Darwin, Marx, and Wagner, it might be instructive to consider the counterpoint of current Russian opinion on this decisive trio. For many obvious reasons this counterpoint of view is not so easy to obtain as one would like it to be. One can never tell how much the counterpoint of view is the least common denominator of party agreement, and how much may represent honest thought. In fairness, one should ask how much of conventional Western point of view on these three controversial figures is dictated by the social mores of our time, and how much is free and honest individual thought.

An observant intellectual traveling in Russia these days may readily obtain opinions regarding the current significance of Darwin, Marx, and Wagner in the general area dominated by Soviet thought. One may obtain clear expressions of opinion regarding Darwin from the biological scientists, and one may see expressions of public regard for him in many places. On all sides and from any Russian, one may obtain opinions about Marx, but clearly most of these are wholly conventional and are dictated by a welter of confusing emotional factors ranging from hysterical bigotry to sophisticated and quite conscious hypocrisy. On the other hand, it is not easy to obtain much of an opinion in Russia about Wagner. His works seem to be rarely performed, and it is difficult to trace much of his influence in current Russian artistic affairs beyond the "famous five" who did so much to enrich the musical and operatic art of the whole world. However, Russian art in general remains amazingly early Victorian.

When I was in Leningrad in the summer of 1956, in company with distinguished colleagues from Ohio State University and other American institutions of higher learning, I visited the Institute of Experimental Medicine, which has functioned continually since its establishment in 1890, by one of the enlightened aristocrats of the period, as a center for research, teaching, and public service in health affairs. It was here that the famed Ivan Petrovitch Pavlov (1849–1936) had worked on gastric function and later carried out his celebrated studies on conditioned reflexes. These studies are still being pursued by his devoted pupils in the renowned Towers of Silence, which he built for the special care of the well-trained dogs that he used.

The grounds of the Institute, though unkempt, have well-planted shrubs and trees and some excellent bits of statuary. There is a magnificent bronze of a German police dog, high on a cylindrical granite pedestal, with an inscription reading "To Our Friends without Whom Our Work Would Be

Nothing." Along one of the drives on the grounds of the Institute are four heroic bronze busts: One is of René Descartes
(1596–1650), the brilliant French mathematician and physi-
ologist, who first described reflex action. Another is to the
memory of Dmitri Mendeleyev (1834–1907), the great chem-
ist who outlined the periodic table of the chemical elements.
A third honors Ivan Makhailovich Sechenov (1829–1905),
the founder of Russian physiology and one who had a profound influence on Pavlov. And the fourth bust, startlingly
enough, is of Charles Darwin.

When opportunity afforded, I asked one of the distinguished physiologists working at the Institute how it happened that there was a bust of Darwin on the grounds. He
replied that Darwin is highly regarded by Russian scientists,
and indeed by the Russian people generally. When I inquired
further, he said that Darwin's principle of adaptation is a
significant one in relation to the whole cultural orientation
of Russia. He said he understood that Darwinism in Western
culture referred generally to the proposition of the survival
of the fittest, the ruthless destruction of the weak by the strong
in the struggle for existence, and the general idea of nature
"red in tooth and claw," with living things engaged in a terrifying struggle for existence at the expense of other living
things, while Russians considered this point of view to be
T. H. Huxley's and Nietzsche's.

On the other hand, he said, for the Russians Darwinism
means primarily the principle of the survival of living things
on the basis of capacity for adaptation to a changing environment. He said, "This is important to understand in relation to our history."

When I asked for details, he continued to explain that
from the beginning of their history, the Russian peoples have
been subjected to vicious, ruthless, and brutal invaders. The

Tartars, the Mongols, the Magyars, the Huns, the Vikings, in successive waves, desolated them, ruining their lands and their possessions and horribly oppressing and cruelly mistreating them. In more recent history Russia was under the heel of the Poles for two centuries of bitter and terrifying slavery, followed by a century of Swedish conquest with brutal and inhuman domination. He referred to the horrors and appalling wastes of the Napoleonic invasion, and spoke feelingly of the destructive invasions by the Germans, which brought desolation and tremendous suffering and misery to millions of Russian people. He continued by saying that besides all of this, Russia itself has been ruled by a succession of cruel, brutal, and tyrannical local and national rulers who changed their policies on a moment's whim.

Nevertheless, he pointed out, the Russian people have survived. He indicated that this has been due to their ability to adapt themselves successfully to changing circumstances in their environment. "The net result," he concluded "is that we seem to be an inconsistent people." He laughed and said, "You are an inconsistent people also, but if you know it, you'd never admit it." He added that the Russians are an untrustworthy, unreliable, unpredictable, but determined people; and he said, "We intend to survive; we know that we can continue to adapt ourselves successfully to whatever change may occur in our environment."

If what my scientific informant said is an opinion shared by intelligent Russians generally, it may indicate why it is that Darwin is so well respected among the Russian people. The frankness with which my host spoke indicates to me that he gave an honest opinion. As such, I believe it deserves to be carefully considered.

In Russia, it would seem to an outside observer that it is not so much Karl Marx as Marxism that counts. Karl Marx as a personality was rapidly thrown into partial limbo by Lenin, and was later eclipsed by Stalin. It is not so much Marxism that is important in contemporary Russia as it is Marxism-Leninism.

Karl Marx's *Critique of Political Economy* seems to have little significance in today's Russia. It is a development of the point of view first expressed in the *Communist Manifesto*, issued by Marx and his friend Friedrich Engels (1820–95) in 1848. This was the period of real social and political revolution in Europe. Idealistic and thoughtful young men were shocked at the implications of the conservative reaction against the high romanticism that followed the final defeat of Napoleon. The revolutionary fervor of these youngsters expressed itself politically against absolutism and conservative dogmatism in politics, economics, science, art, and the humanities. The explosive uprisings of 1848 were merely the prelude to a rumbling ground swell of revolution against all the cherished ideals and standards of Western culture from antiquity, at least as conventionally stereotyped and dogmatized. It was, as Barzun states, "the reasonable and the real" that revolted against the resurrected mythology of pre–eighteenth-century enlightenment in Western culture.

The influence of Marx was clearly to reorient history and economics in a materialistic manner and to establish a materialistic basis for sociology. This was simply an extension of an important tendency developing in biology in the middle of the nineteenth century, sparked again by a manifesto, this time in 1847.

Among the gifted pupils of the great biologist, Johannes Müller (1801–58) at Berlin, was a remarkable trio of keen young thinkers—Carl Ludwig (1816–95), Emil DuBois-Reymond (1818–96), and Hermann von Helmholtz (1821–94). Perhaps under Müller's inspiration, these brilliant youngsters, destined themselves to become among the greatest of all teachers and research workers in the functional aspects of living things, issued a remarkable manifesto stating that all living processes are explainable in terms of physics and chemistry. This was an amazing expression of faith, since there was little evidence at the time to support it.

This manifesto had a significant influence on one of Ludwig's closest friends and pupils, Ivan Makhailovich Sechenov, who started the highly significant Russian study of brain function. The impact of this materialistic manifesto on scientists, particularly biologists and medical workers, must have been profound. Indeed, Ernest Jones, in his detailed life of Freud, refers to the intense effect it had on Freud himself.

Sechenov, an idealistic young man, appalled at the wretchedness and poverty existing in Russia, determined to do something about it. A skilled experimental biologist, he first clearly demonstrated the essential inhibitory function of the cerebral cortex in vertebrates. He was an inspiring teacher, who campaigned successfully for coeducation, helped combat alcoholism, and stood by his scientific ideals and standards even in the face of official disapproval and the loss of his state position at the University of St. Petersburg. Above all, he had a profound influence on his followers, the most distinguished of whom was Pavlov.

It is important here to consider the over-all development of Russian science, with respect to obtaining verifiable information about ourselves and our environment. The dramatic successes of the Russians in mathematics, and especially in nuclear physics and rocketry, have blinded us, perhaps, to the equally significant advances that Russian biological scientists have made in understanding living material. Thanks to the influence of Sechenov and Pavlov, Russian neurophysiologists have developed, in great detail, verifi-

able knowledge about the way in which our brains and nervous systems work. That this is oriented entirely along materialistic lines, in reference to physics and chemistry, is
clear indication not only of the direct influence of Sechenov,
but also of the co-ordination and complementariness of
Sechenov's influence with that of Marx. Russian materialistic
biology and Russian materialistic economics both stem from
the intellectual ferment of the period immediately following
the abortive political revolutions of 1848, which were
themselves a manifestation of the then current intellectual
revolution.

With this sort of materialistic orientation in biological
science and in socioeconomics, it can be readily appreciated
that there was little inspiration for free expression in the
non-materialistic arts and humanities. Wagner's attempt to
unify the arts through his grand operatic venture may have
had echoes in Russia, but free expression and experimenta-
tion in graphic or plastic art, in music, drama, poetry, literature, or dancing, was lost in the overwhelming intellectual
emphasis on materialism. True, great Russian artists like
Stravinsky introduced startling and scintillating innovations,
but not in Russia. Most of them worked in Paris.

This is not to say that the development of Western art was
not followed avidly in Russia. There are as fine collections of
French expressionistic art in the galleries of Moscow and
Leningrad as are to be found anywhere in the world. Russian
music remains exciting and vigorous. Russian literature remains profoundly significant, particularly in the depths of
its psychological insight. Russian graphic and plastic art is
characterized by deep psychological penetration. Although
Russian poetry is not well known to us, perhaps because of
difficulties in translation, Russian dancing remains supreme.
Nevertheless, Russian art remains characteristically Russian

and, in its stereotyped style, reminiscent of early Victorian standards.

In all this Russian intellectual counterpoint, there is a missing note, and its absence is ominous. Except in the forced bigotry of Marxism-Leninism, where does Russian consideration of philosophical principles involve the sciences and the arts? In yielding so fully to what Paul Elmer More called "the demon of the absolute," Russian counterpoint lost its self-corrective feedback, and became, paradoxically, in relation to its adaptability, a cacophony.

And Yet No Harmony

In this consideration of point and counterpoint during the past century, it is painfully clear that no harmony has been achieved. What is lacking? Is it failure of communication? Does this failure of communication result in failure of understanding? Are we bound by our stereotyped prejudices and biases? Are there irreconcilable factors in the confusion? Have we learned anything from the great wars that plagued us throughout the last century? Do we have any unifying force in humanity? What is left of the Christian ideal if it has been so consistently flouted by all who profess themselves to be Christians? What impact has been made upon our intellectual progress by the transition from the concept of evolution to the concept of relativity? Has there been any significant effect on our intellectual growth as a result of the high degree of verifiability and predictability reached in the physical sciences, with the awful consequences of nuclear energy, in full gestation for our weal or woe?

In a consideration of the influence of Darwin, Marx, and Wagner, it is clear that we are concerned chiefly with the sciences and the humanities. What is lacking? We talk a great deal about the importance of balancing our scientific development by an appropriate regard for the humanities. Let it be clear at once that this is a precarious balance. This balance has little stability. In our time we are condensing the long respected Greek triad of logics, aesthetics, and ethics into the dyad of the sciences and the humanities. This Greek triad had long intellectual stability. Is the balancing of our scientific disciplines with our humanistic studies to be enough?

The intellectual confusions of the past century, with all the frustrations, miseries, and terror of the masses of the people, occasioned through almost continual strife and warfare, are the awful consequences of our intellectual myopia. The intellectual tragedy of the past century has been the neglect of ethics.

Lacking agreed-upon standards for interpersonal relations, failing to set up appropriate purposes and goals for human endeavor, being vague and uncertain about the propriety and effectiveness of individual and social conduct, we have, the world over, brought ourselves into a very sorry situation. Indeed, never before in the history of humanity has there been such a widespread and universal lack of concern or regard for moral and ethical considerations. This wholly bad condition prevails in both Western and Soviet culture.

This neglect of ethics may have been associated during the past century with increasing skepticism about our traditional religious beliefs. People generally act on the basis of what they believe. They generally believe on the basis of what they think they know. Our traditional churches have based religious faith on revealed, intuitive, subjective, and introspective knowledge. Meanwhile, a rapidly developing scientific methodology has given us a procedure whereby factual knowledge about ourselves and our environment is capable of verification by independent observation, and thus by voluntary agreement. This verifiable information about ourselves and our environment has been devastating to many of our most cherished beliefs. It may well be then that the decline in our regard for moral and ethical affairs has been associated with the crumbling of our traditional religious faith as expressed in our organized churches.

On the other hand, thoughtful individuals the world over have probably become more religious than ever. With scientific and thus verifiable knowledge about ourselves and our environment, we are finding it possible to build a firm and solid body of beliefs, based more satisfactorily upon what we can agree upon as "true." Perhaps we are now in a great gestational period for a huge ground swell of moral growth and religious confidence. There may be coming a gradual harmony in the point and counterpoint of Western and Soviet cultures.

Both these great cultures have been in turmoil during the past century of confusion largely through lack of agreement and lack of responsibility on ethical matters. We have slipped from a psychology of individual and group responsibility to a psychology of persuasion or of deterrence in order to obtain advantage at the expense of others.

The concept of evolution, developed by biologists, has become confused with the concept of relativity, developed by physicists, and we apply both concepts, as absolutes, to ethical problems without understanding either the concepts or what we are doing with them. This sort of projection is dangerous. We have come philosophically through positivism and pragmatism to existentialism, with counterpoint of mysticism, and we produce beatniks. The materialism of science is taken as an absolute, so that the purposeful function of ethics is forgotten, and there seems to be nothing left for the arts and humanities except to go wild or to yield to the presumed absolute of materialism.

The ideas of Darwin, Marx, and Wagner worked in strange ways to shape our century of confusion. The situation has been neatly suggested by Jaan Kangilaski, one of the thoughtful young editors of the *Ohio State Lantern*. Often I wish that I could say things that I want to say as clearly and as directly as the keen young people who are now thinking about the world!

Kangilaski points out that Darwin's followers were responsible for a notion, conveniently called "social Darwinism," that society is a jungle where only the strong and ruthless survive. To social Darwinists, the older morality was an invention of the weak in an attempt to restrain the strong. Marx condemned the old morality, too, as a way devised by the strong to keep the weak in bondage.

However, Marx saw no place in his system for the "hero types" which the social Darwinists depicted. Lenin, however, showed that the weak could move only if led by the strong. This picture resulted in the Soviet system.

On the other hand, Wagner made heroes of strong men. His "glorious leader" ideas became fused with notions from social Darwinism on "the master race." Ignoring any sense of make-believe or play, Wagner expressed his insecurity in tragic pageantry, which revolted Nietzsche even though Nietzsche promoted the idea of a super race. Wagner sought salvation by delusion, and gave the setting for the Nazis.

As far as the people were concerned, Darwin's scientific induction was pervertedly eclipsed by "social Darwinism"; Marx's materialistic economics was swallowed in Leninistic communism; and Wagner's glorification of phoney heroism was ballooned to a ruthless fascism. The peoples of three great nations, England, Russia, and Germany, led themselves

astray by their pathetic desires, purging themselves only by
the most terrible of total wars. Japan, catching the Wagnerian infection from Germany, exploded us into the conflict,
to decide its issues without understanding them. It is with the
painful effort at understanding that we are now concerned.

Inevitably, the Nazis and the Communists came into terrible conflict. It remains now to be determined whether or not,
with our presumed greater self-understanding, we can bring
about some degree of compromise between the ideas evolving
in the Soviet world and those in the Western world. We have
had our terrifying experience with the clash of ideas result-
ing in war. Can we bring about some harmony in compromis-
ing our evolving ideas about the ways we would like to live
so that there may be some degree of peace?

Ethics in a Nuclear Age

One may still find substantial relations between the classic
Greek concepts of logics, ethics, and aesthetics. In order to
gain satisfactions in living, it is necessary, first, to find something of what we call the "truth" about ourselves and the universe surrounding us. This is the business of logics. In the
light of such knowledge as we may acquire, we are then
prepared to examine the motives that determine our conduct
and our relations with other people, in seeking the goals we
prefer in our hierarchy of values. Here is the problem for
ethics. There comes, then, the question of how best to apply
our knowledge to the achievement of our purposes in order to
reach the satisfactions we crave. This is the function of aesthetics.

In our current terminology, the logics have become our
sciences, the aesthetics our arts. What has happened to the
ethics? Have these evaporated into our "value judgments,"
or are they condensed with our arts into the "humanities"?

Have ethical considerations left our culture because traditional ethics have become inappropriate or because our philosophers are no longer in communication with us, the people, because they have lost the common touch by espousing an incomprehensible jargon? Actually, ethics may again fructify in our culture if we approach morals in a down-to-earth descriptive manner, seeking operational principles in human conduct rather than exhortations to activity based on those old bogies of fear of punishment or hope of reward from some supernatural power.

We may actually use Darwinistic principles of survival values to reach a first approximation to a naturally operating principle governing interpersonal relations. This was attempted two decades ago, in a California redwood grove, by a famed seminar group which included my great teacher Edwin G. Conklin, professor of biology at Princeton and at that time president of the American Association for the Advancement of Science; C. Judson Herrick, professor of neurology at the University of Chicago and author of a significant study on *The Evolution of Human Nature*; Olof Larsell, professor of neuro-anatomy at the University of Oregon; and Herbert M. Evans, director of the Institute of Experimental Biology at the University of California. This group, with a considerable number of young colleagues, explored the significance of evolutionary principles in regard to human relations. They agreed that the plethora of evidence justifies inducing a naturally operating principle governing human relations.

This naturally operating principle may be stated descriptively: "The probability of survival of a relationship between individuals or groups of individuals increases to the extent that the relationship is mutually satisfying." This statement differs from ordinary ethical statements in that it is inducible and descriptive rather than normative. It reveals a naturally operating principle, which seems to work whether we like it or not or even whether we are aware of it or not. In this regard it is something like the principle of gravity. As far as I know, this is the first attempt to define a naturally operating principle in human relations which has ethical significance. It is a culmination of long efforts to develop a scientific approach to ethics. Darwin showed the way.

This principle carries no implication of what we should or should not do, through fear of punishment or hope of reward, but rather indicates the conditions under which benefit from the principle may be derived. The principle seems to be applicable to such relationships as those existing in a family between husband and wife, between parents and children, or more broadly between friends, between employers and employees, or even between social or political groups, or between nations.

If one party to an interpersonal relationship desires the relationship to continue, it is obviously necessary to do something to make the relationship satisfying to the other party. This has something of the ring of the Golden Rule in it. The Golden Rule would thus seem to be an implicitly derived exhortation from the observed operation of the descriptive principle.

It seems then that the entire matter of interpersonal relations, which are being so extensively explored these days, can be brought into sharp ethical and moral focus in accordance with our ancient concepts and ideals of ethics. Instead of ethics developing as an esoteric branch of philosophy, with a professional jargon incomprehensible to people generally, would it not be wiser to bring the field of ethics into our ordinary realm of conversation and comprehension, along with our logics, as represented in our sciences, and along with our aesthetics, as represented in our arts and in our humanities? Perhaps then we can get a stable triadic relationship between logics, aesthetics, and ethics, and thus maintain a balance between our sciences and our humanities.

The greatest scientific development during our century of confusion has been the recognition of quantum theory, particularly in relation to energy transformations. This has culminated in the terrible consequences of utilizing nuclear energy. We are coming gradually to appreciate that it is impossible to use nuclear energy in forcing the advantage of one people at the expense of another without destruction for all. Survival values continue to force adaptability. Perhaps our century of confusion will close with universal realization that war is now a fatal factor in international relationships and can bring no satisfaction to anyone.

One of the most important aspects of our recognition of quantum theory is its application to biology. Radiant energy of all sorts encompasses us all the time. The energy transferences that may occur in connection with any living material may produce molecular changes in the complicated genes that direct our growth and our lives. It is this factor that really explains the chance origin of a new type of living material, which then becomes subject to Darwinian evolutionary factors if it is to survive. It is this matter also that is paramount in such diseases as cancer and in all phases of population control directed toward a generally better breed of human beings. It is something which we had better learn to understand thoroughly if those who come after us are to survive.

Inevitably, also, this theory is bound up with the inflexible principles of thermodynamics, which regulate energy transformations. One of these principles is dramatically called

"Time's Arrow" by my good friend Harold Blum, since it specifies the direction in time in which events in our universe must move. One of its interesting Darwinian consequences is that any species now extinct can never reappear in our present environment. The entropy of our universe has changed from that which prevailed when the species arose, and no quantum strike on any existing gene can bring the extinct species back into this environment. This is an arresting fact. It indicates clearly that there are limits, not only to what we might want to do, but also to what we actually can ever do.

PROSPECT

This, then, is a time of intellectual crisis in reorganizing our ideas from viruses to cosmologies. We have so much new science to assimilate that we are bound to have some intellectual indigestion. A major problem exists in trying satisfactorily to translate the developments of current science so that people generally may understand them and realize their consequences. We have increasingly, each of us, an obligation to learn about the vastly complex factors that operate within ourselves and in the world around us.

Science is a great co-operative venture between technical experts and people everywhere. To be successful in benefiting us all, it becomes more necessary all the time for us to agree on the purposes to which we apply our science. Maybe as we learn more about ourselves, we can more easily reach mutually satisfying agreements between individuals and between groups of people.

Try as we may, no one of us can escape the emotionally conditioning processes that determine our individual and collective behavior. At best we can perhaps learn to understand it, and thus perhaps to control it for mutual benefit. At least we have learned to find outlets in the arts and in the

humanities. These are the wise balances for our scientific endeavor. But they must be stabilized by ethical considerations
also if there are to be any lasting satisfactions for any of us.

My own emotional response to what I've been talking about
is expressed in what may be called "cadence," since some of
my friends indicated their unwillingness to consider it as a
more formal verse form, such as a sonnet. They are probably wise. With reference to the application of quantum
theory and thermodynamics to biological evolution, I once
wrote:

> From all the vast
> unbounded sun-lit space about
> come fragments of an energy
> to catalyze our life,
> to make the green of plants,
> and in a mystic liturgy
> of ordered chance,
> to change another gene,
> which may produce,
> if viable, a kind
> of different living thing,
> which must, if it survives,
> adapt itself to others, as all
> of them shall find.
>
> Here in this systemed neat
> evolving scheme of everything,
> Time's Arrow points the way
> inflexibly,
> nor can we shift a dot
> of its position, nor its movement stay,
> nor though we read
> the sign-post fairly well,
> to what it points, have we as yet the wit to say.

The ancient Judaeo-Christian liturgy, after an appropriate
invocation, calls first for humble acknowledgment of ig-

norance and error, with a plea for understanding and for-
giveness, implying a determination to err no more and to live
more wisely, and thus better. By acknowledging our errors in
interpersonal relations individually and socially, and in the
applications of our logics and our sciences, in our century of
confusion, perhaps we can turn with determination, in bringing moral responsibility to our sciences and to our arts, toward a coming century of good sense.

REFERENCES

BARNETT, L. "Darwin's World of Nature," *Life,* June 30, 1959.

BARNETT, S. A. (ed.). *A Century of Darwin.* London: William Heinemann, 1958.

BARZUN, JACQUES. *Darwin, Marx, Wagner: Critique of a Heritage.* 2nd rev. ed. Garden City, N. Y.: Doubleday Anchor Books, 1958.

BENÉT, STEPHEN VINCENT. *John Brown's Body.* Garden City, N. Y.: Doubleday, Doran & Co., 1928.

BLUM, H. F. *Time's Arrow and Evolution.* Princeton, N. J.: Princeton University Press, 1951.

Commemoration of the Centennial of the Publication of *The Origin of Species* by Charles Darwin, *Proceedings of the American Philosophical Society,* Vol. CIII, Part 2 (April, 1959).

CONKLIN, E. G. *Man: Real and Ideal.* New York: Charles Scribner's Sons, 1943.

EISELEY, LOREN. *Darwin's Century: Evolution and the Men Who Discovered It.* Garden City, N. Y.: Doubleday & Co., 1956.

HERRICK, C. J. *The Evolution of Human Nature.* Austin, Texas: University of Texas Press, 1956.

HIMMELFARB, G. *Darwin and the Darwinian Revolution.* Garden City, N. Y.: Doubleday & Co., 1959.

HOOK, SIDNEY. *The Ambiguous Legacy: Marx and the Marxists.* Princeton, N. J.: D. Van Nostrand Co., 1955.
———. "What's Left of Karl Marx?", *Saturday Review,* June 6, 1959.

HUXLEY, FRANCIS. "Charles Darwin: Life and Habit," *American Scholar,* XXVIII (1959), 489–99.

KANGILASKI, JAAN. "The Way It Goes," *Ohio State Lantern,* October 15, 1959.

LEAKE, CHAUNCEY D. "Ethicogenesis," *Scientific Monthly*, LX (April, 1945), 245–53.

————, and ROMANELL, P. *Can We Agree?: A Scientist and a Philosopher Argue about Ethics.* Austin, Texas: University of Texas Press, 1950.

MONTAGU, M. F. ASHLEY. *The Director of Human Development: Biological and Social Bases.* New York: Harper & Bros., 1955.

NOWELL-SMITH, P. H. *Ethics.* London: Penguin Books, 1954.

WADDINGTON, C. H. *Science and Ethics.* London: Allen & Unwin, 1942.

Bertram D. Wolfe

A Century of Marx and Marxism

THE ONE HUNDRED and ten years since
the *Communist Manifesto* pronounced the
downfall of the bourgeoisie and the vic-
tory of the proletariat as alike inevitable, the round hundred
years since the *Critique of Political Economy* elaborated
Marx's theory of social development, social revolution, and
the general propositions of historical materialism, and the
near century (ninety-three years, to be exact) since *Das Kapital* laid bare the "economic law of motion of modern society"
—that century has not dealt kindly with the predictions of
Karl Marx. At wholesale and at retail they have failed to
materialize. The very approach which claimed to make of
sociology a science and to lay bare the law of motion of industrial society has proved irrelevant to the society of our
day. Nevertheless, while other nineteenth-century social
thinkers and social critics remain buried in textbooks, the
name of Marx has become a household word. The rulers of
one-third of mankind have raised him to the post of founder
of the faith by which they claim to chart their course. Men
accept him and men reject him, quite frequently without
knowing his work.

In the West, which will be my concern, there are a number
of intellectuals who call themselves Marxists; yet recognizing the shipwreck of so much of his teaching and the dis-

crediting of so much of it by the abuse of his name in the
East, they seek new ways to hold on to their threatened faith.
One hears on American campuses the "Marxist theory of
the state," when more often what is meant is the Leninist
theory of the state; or the "Marxist theory of the party,"
when what is meant is the Leninist theory of the party; or
the "Marxist theory of imperialism," when what is meant is
the Leninist theory of imperialism. Indeed, there is no Marxist theory of imperialism. Having faithfully combed his work
from end to end, I have failed to find the word "imperialism"
more than a single time, and then it referred to the structure
of empire of Napoleon the Less, that is, of Napoleon III. In
so far as Marx talked of colonialism, he thought of it as a
force making for progress and breaking its way into the
millennial slumber of the East, awakening peoples, and moving them into the main course of historical development.
There is really no Leninist theory of imperialism; rather
there is a liberal theory of imperialism developed by Hob-
son and a socialist theory developed by Hilferding and Lux-
emberg in reaction to the great imperialist spree at the end
of the nineteenth and the beginning of the twentieth century.
Lenin seized this to make certain tactical and strategical uses
of it for his war to subvert the society in which he lived. All
this passes on many campuses for the "Marxist theory of
imperialism."

Non-Marxists in the free world, if they study his writing
dispassionately—as dispassionately as men can read anything so charged with passion—are likely to recognize in
him a great moralist, a great stylist, a seminal and orphic
thinker, whose insights and whose very errors can still fructify the social disciplines. Let us not call them—following
Marx's error—"social sciences." History, sociology, economics and political philosophy, social disciplines all, can

benefit by contact with the writings and thought of Karl Marx. The practitioners of those disciplines are a little shamefaced about the fact that man's values form a constitutive part of his examination into his own activities. Marx came to feel the same way. Were it not for this false shame, falsely regarded as scientific, our social disciplines would be neither so nihilistic nor so trivial. Political philosophy would not be so nearly in eclipse and it would be acknowledging, if it were in a state of vigor, a substantial debt to Marx and his fellow utopians for insight into that branch of political philosophy that we might call social criticism, and which concerns itself with the imperfections of any society-in-being as measured against its own potentialities and against man's flickering yet undying vision of the good life.

The neatest trick of the nineteenth century, given the prestige of science in that century, was for Marx to call his vision of the good life "scientific," and to insist that all of his predecessors were utopian and all of his rivals the same. As Darwin's fame grew, Marx staked out a modest claim to be the Darwin of the social sciences, to deduce what *must* be from the law of motion which he claims to have discovered to be inherent in what *is*. The utopians go from the "is" to the "ought." Marx claimed to go from the "is" to the "must be." His doctrine therefore claims to be a doctrine of the inevitable. Human values are expelled from the social sciences once more, and he identifies his theory of history with history itself; therefore, history becomes the only judge and history can be a cruel and an inhuman judge of all things. But the "must be" discovered within the "is" conveniently turns out to be the "ought to be" that Marx began with before he claimed to be a scientist. Marx asks history to do nothing but what it must do, because concealed in the wrappings of

Marx's "must" is the vision of Marx's "ought." Marx discovered this convenient trick when he got into a controversy with Proudhon who was a Socialist like himself (somewhat earlier), in many ways his predecessor, one to whom he owed a debt and who was more of a humanist-socialist than he.

When Marx was just becoming interested in socialism, the first three workingmen he met happened to be three autodidactic socialist workingmen, Weitling, Proudhon, and Leroux, and he immediately proceeded to make a vast generalization from three cases. From them he deduced one of his scientific laws, namely, that "revolutionary feeling is natural to the working class; and that their revolutionary activity is the very greatest joy of their lives." Had he not seen this in three workingmen?

In 1845, Marx wrote an impassioned defense of Proudhon against all his critics—thirty pages of defense and exaltation of Proudhon. The key sentence in those thirty pages states that "Proudhon's *Qu'est-ce que la propriété?* is the first decisive, unfettered, and scientific examination to make possible a real science of national economy." That's high praise indeed. That was 1845.

In 1846, spurred on by the police of Paris, Marx moved to Brussels, taking his huge head and his huge beard along with him, and set up in that city the Communist Propaganda Committee. He wrote to Proudhon: "Will you be the Paris correspondent of the Communist Propaganda Committee?" Proudhon's answer is still interesting:

My dear Mr. Marx, let us seek together if you wish the laws of society, the manner in which these laws are realized, the process by which we shall succeed in discovering them, but for God's sake, after having demolished all the *a priori* dogmatisms, let us not fall into the same contradictions as your countryman, Martin Luther, who, after having over-

thrown Catholic theology, began at once with the help of
excommunications and anathemas to found a Protestant
theology. I applaud with all my heart your thought of bringing to light all opinions. Let us carry on a good and loyal
polemic. Let us give the world an example of a learned and
far-sighted tolerance. Let us not, because we are at the head
of a movement, make ourselves the leaders of a new intoler-
ance. Let us not pose as the apostles of a new religion, even
if it be the religion of logic and reason. Let us gather together and encourage all protests; let us condemn all ex-
clusiveness; let us never regard a question as exhausted. On
this condition I will gladly enter into your association; otherwise, no.

Well, the fat was in the fire. Marx could hardly wait until
he had finished the letter to begin his devastating attack upon
Proudhon, the book called *The Poverty of Philosophy*, at-
tacking Proudhon's latest book, *The Philosophy of Poverty*.
Thereafter, the epithet "utopian" became the most potent
weapon in Marx's struggle for originality as the exclusive
"scientist" among contemporary socialist thinkers. Science,
truth, and progress were completely in his camp; utopianism, illusion, and reaction in all the others. To be a utopian
in an age of science means to be out of touch with economic
development. But if you want to find out what economic development is, what its underlying law of motion is, you must
of course learn from Marx. Thus began the Marxist device
of annihilation by labels.

Karl Marx was great as a social critic—not as a scientist
and not by virtue of the laws he thought he had discovered
—but by virtue of the values he wished to realize, values
which he now concealed in the verbiage of science and predic-
tive inevitability. I call as my first witness that Marx was not
a scientist but a true utopian Socialist (this is not said in
disrespect; I think better of him when I call him a utopian

Socialist than when he calls himself a scientific Socialist)
one Friedrich Engels. Writing in the same year, 1846, Engels says,

> Right now the Germans have begun to spoil the communist
> movement too. As always, the latest and least effective be-
> lieve that they are able to cover their sleepiness through con-
> tempt for their predecessors and through philosophical
> bragging. What the French or the English said ten, twenty
> or forty years ago [and it is true that the French and Eng-
> lish preceded the Germans in socialist theory] and said very
> well, very clearly, and in very beautiful style, this at long last
> the Germans are becoming acquainted with fragmentarily
> and have Hegelized. At best they have been belatedly redis-
> covering and publishing in much worsened or abstract form,
> as a wholly new discovery, what was done by their predeces-
> sors. Nor do I exclude my own works from this stricture.
> What is peculiar to the Germans is only the bad abstract or
> unintelligible and oblique form in which they've expressed
> their thoughts.

Now this is very modest on Engels' part, and indeed Engels
was a modest man concerning his own works all his life. He
became immodest concerning the claims of Marx but not so
immodest concerning himself. He is careful not to mention
Marx in one way or another. He lists no names in talking of
the Germans, nor does he Hegelize their predecessors and
express them in more difficult form. But he had already
formed his union with Marx. This close partnership was already a year old when he produced the testimony which I
have brought before you.

Now I call as my second witness one Karl Marx. Here is
his description, in the same year, of what the future society is
going to be like.

> In the communist society, where no one has any exclusive
> circle of activity but can train himself in any branch he

wants to, society regulates general production, and just by that, makes it possible for me to do one thing today and another tomorrow—to hunt mornings, fish afternoons, raise cattle evenings, criticize after dinner in whatever way I please, without ever having to become a fisherman, a herdsman, or a critic.

If this is not a utopian picture of the future of society, then I don't know what a utopian picture is.

More than a century ago, when Marx undertook to analyze the law of motion of industrial society and the structure and destiny of this society, he saw it heading toward immediate catastrophe. I want to stress the word "immediate." The cataclysm was mere days or weeks away. It was to come with the next skirmish or the next raising of barricades. Then when it did not come from the barricades of 1848, it was to come out of a war which would begin before the year was out. A little later, when the wars of 1848 and 1849 did not bring the social revolution, it was to come out of the next downswing of the business cycle. "The revolution," he wrote, "remains as inevitable as the next crisis itself."

Along with this perpetual prediction of cataclysm, Marx went out on a limb to predict what would be the fate of each prime minister, of each sovereign, of each country. He climbed out on the limb of prophecy more often than did any other man of his time, and the limb withered under him and cracked off more often and more obviously than in the case of any other man of his time.

Worse than the fate of his prophecies concerning wars, the fall of ministries, sovereigns, dynasties, and regimes was the fate of the general law itself. Industrial society, he held, was destined to transform itself with great speed, indeed was even then completing its transformation into a society that was entirely polarized and torn in two as by mitosis, a tiny handful of huge exploiters at one pole, an overwhelming mass of miserable dehumanized proletarians at the other. Proletarian misery and dehumanization were to become absolute. All other classes would be ruined, would disappear, and would be swallowed up into the proletariat. The outraged and the injured, having lost their last stake in society and the last semblance of humanity, were to rise in their wrath, expropriate the handful of expropriators at the other pole and burst "the integument" of existing society; then, miraculously, these totally dehumanized proletarians would humanize all mankind.

The *Communist Manifesto* was prepared jointly by Marx and Engels, but Marx is the true author. It proclaimed the end of nationalism and was issued as a manifesto for the coming storms of 1848. But the uprisings of 1848 proved to be the greatest outburst of nationalism in the whole of European history. Marx and Engels themselves suddenly discovered their national feelings, after having proclaimed that the worker had no country, that the bourgeoisie had destroyed the nation in producing the international market, and the like. Although the *Communist Manifesto* said not one word about the fate of the German nation, within a couple of months Marx and Engels were most deeply concerned with the problem of German unification, with urging the German people to make war on their neighbors for the sake of their unification and their revolutionization, and had put the national question at the center of their writings. It continued to be at the center of their writings, as Germans, until "the old boy Bismarck did our work for us."

The proletariat, which in 1848 "already had no country to defend," was to be found in 1914, and once more in 1939, and is still today, defending its respective countries. Indeed, nationalism was to prove the one sure cause for which the millions were ready to fight and die. And, in the course of the twentieth century, it would spread from Europe, which was its home, to Asia and Africa where the nation had been unknown in Marx and Engels' day.

When barricades and street fighting did not end the system in 1848, Marx began to call for war. *Die Neue Rheinische Zeitung*, which he was then editing, became the most warlike paper in all of Europe, indeed the most warlike in the whole history of European journalism. He called for war of the German people on Prussia, for war on all the German principalities, for war on Denmark over Schleswig-Holstein, for war on Russia, for wars simultaneously on Russia, Prussia, England, and Denmark. Until the last few years before Marx's death in 1883, he and Engels continued to take sides zealously and enthusiastically in every so-called capitalist war, while Marx himself continued unceasingly to urge Germany, his native land, England, his refuge, and France, the home of his first ideas, to declare war on Russia. But in the final decade of his life, and in the twelve years that Engels lived after him, he and Engels began to catch a glimpse of the fearful outlines of the holocaust that was to come in 1914, "a peoples' war" as they called it, in which entire peoples and not professional armies would be involved. He felt that for his native land this would be "a defensive war, not one of those newfangled localized wars, but a race war, against the allied races of Slavs and Latins." He realized that its outcome would be uncertain, that the European civilization which he ambivalently loved and hated would be in ruins, that the nations would fight for their very lives and all the peoples would defend their countries; and he lost his taste for war as an engine of progress. Three years before he

died he wrote soberly to the Russian Narodnik, N. F. Daniel-
son: "A European war I would consider a terrible misfor-
tune."

Thus by recognizing the error of some few of their posi-
tions and predictions, Marx and Engels became the first revisionists. The orthodox take unction from this as a sign that
the founders were scientists, not dogmatists, although they
are terribly loath to touch whatever Marx and Engels left
untouched, or to allow, now that Marx and Engels are dead,
any authorized revisionists among the living.

The revisions were not limited to war and nationalism
and the timetable of the revolution. Thus, in 1850, Marx had
assured the proletariat that it was "a senseless utopia" to
expect "the slightest improvement in its position within the
bourgeois republic." That was in the forties. But in the
sixties Marx began to hail the legal shortening of the working
day as "a consequence of the pressure of society," a quite
classless formulation, and as "the victory of a principle, in
which the political economy of the bourgeoisie has capitu-
lated to the political economy of the working class, as a result of a half-century of civil war." If this makes us wonder
what Marx can mean by civil war, our wonder is increased by
his coming to recognize that in America, England, and Hol-
land (Engels later added France), the social revolution,
which of course had to be a revolution, might be achieved
by peaceful democratic process, "barricades being unneces-
sary because there, if they want to, the proletariat can win
victory at the polls."

Whatever these reluctant revisions in the light of their experience with a recalcitrant and bewilderingly changing
world, at the core of Marx's thinking and emotions there remained to the end an irreducible holistic and apocalyptic

element. He still continued to think of industrial society in mythical Hegelian terms as "the system." He persisted in believing that whatever defects he perceived (and he was good at perceiving defects) were integral to the system and inseparable from it, and could not be removed defect by defect but only by scrapping the system and replacing it with another system. He was sure he knew the framework of the rigidities beyond which the most rapidly changing world in human history could not change further without a shattering of the supposedly rigid framework. He assigned to a particular class the mission of shattering the framework. He was sure he could descry, and at no great distance, a day of wrath and doom. He was insistent that continuous alteration (reform) changed essentially nothing, except that it might help the chosen class by giving it more leisure to learn to comprehend its mission. That mission was not the elimination of recognizable evils (that would be reform), but sudden and total transformation (that would be revolution).

In Volume I of *Das Kapital*, which is the only volume Marx completed, he is possessed by this contradiction between his appreciation of the reforms and his insistence on the revolution. The book contains rich treasures of empirical materials—largely derived, incidentally, from the Parliamentary Bluebooks of a nation at work reforming the evils of its early industrialization. It contains historical sketches, studies of technology, analyses of the development of modern industry, statistical material of interest, summaries and critiques of current economic theory, and keen sociological observations. But the sections which derive from the British Parliamentary Bluebooks testify eloquently to the awakening conscience, not of a class, but of British society. His paean to the victory of the Ten Hours Bill and other social legislation tells the reader that the lot of the working classes is improving, its power and organization growing stronger, its needs winning the support of all disinterested sections of society. "Capital is under compulsion from society." "The factory magnates have resigned themselves to the inevitable." "The power of resistance of capital has gradually weakened . . . the power of attack of the working class has grown with the number of its allies. . . . Hence the comparatively rapid advance since 1860."

This seems clear enough—and comforting—but suddenly, at the very end of the volume, Marx bethinks himself of the other pole of his thought; and we come to his general conclusion to all the empirical material, the general law or general line of the volume. This chapter he calls "The Historical Tendency of Capitalistic Accumulation." All the history which he gives empirically is forgotten when he attempts to tell us what the historical tendency of capitalist accumulation is. Capital, we learn, came into the world conceived in original sin, "a congenital bloodstain on its cheek, dripping with blood and dirt from head to foot from every pore"; and it is destined now by the workings of "the immanent law of capitalist production itself" to leave the world in a cataclysm.

> Along with the constantly diminishing number of magnates of capital . . . grows the mass of misery, oppression, slavery, degradation, exploitation; but with this grows too the revolt of the working class. . . . The monopoly of capital becomes a fetter upon the mode of production. Centralization of the means of production, and socialization of labor, at last reach a point where they become incompatible with their capitalist integument. This integument is burst asunder. The knell of capitalist private property sounds. The expropriators are expropriated.

Was it for this that all the vast researches in *Das Kapital* were undertaken and all the empirical material accumu-

lated? Marx had reached this conclusion when he was crack-
ing the binding of the first French book on economics back
in 1844. This "general law" was up his sleeve before he even
began his concrete investigation. Perhaps surrounding this
general law with empirical material would make it seem
more impressive. But the material, far from bolstering, re-
futes the general law. The grand conclusion is our old friend
the pre-economics prophecy of 1844, the prophecy of the imminent Apocalypse.

In a sober moment Marx once wrote, "No social order
ever perishes before all the productive forces for which there
is room in it have developed." This, on examination, proves
no more explicit than any other of Marx's sweeping gen-
eralizations, nor any truer, as the Russian and Chinese revolutions were to demonstrate. With singular perversity, history was to vouchsafe social revolution in backward countries
on the eve of their industrialization, and was to deny social
revolutions in the advanced industrial societies which Marx's
law specifically dedicated to revolution.

Moreover, not only had the industrial society which Marx
knew not reached, as he thought, the end of its development
in 1844, or in 1848, when he delivered the doom so stir-
ringly, but it was scarcely at the beginning of the development of its productive forces. That industrial revolution
which Marx had studied, the change from manpower, animal
power, wind power, and water power to steam power, and
from cottage handicraft to machinofacture, was only the
first industrial revolution. It was to be followed by a second,
the age of electricity, and a third, and a fourth, and a fifth
—the conveyor belt, the combustion engine, synthetic chemistry, electronics, automation, atomic fission, atomic fusion;
and the end is not yet. True, these last two, fission and fusion,

do unpleasantly hint at a possible cataclysm, but it is not Marx's cataclysm.

In place of the polarization which Marx had predicted, the very opposite has occurred in society. The intermediate classes that were to have been proletarianized have frequently and greatly changed their character and enormously multiplied. The industrial proletariat has, contrary to Marx's expectation, lost in numerical weight in society, in the total population, but has gained greatly in status and in organized economic and political power. The service trades which Marx contemptuously treated as sheer economic waste and as "parasitic servitors to the parasites," have increased steadily in number and variety, and in the advanced countries have become servitors to the working population as well. The problem of whether we should sympathize with the proletariat and help it to improve its place in society has become completely separated from the problem of whether we should trust it with our fate, let it remake society after an explosion, and let it dictate the nature of the new society and "humanize" it. To the first problem, whether we should sympathize with the proletariat and improve its lot, history has said yes. To the second problem, whether we should entrust the fate of society to what Marx called "the most brutalized, dehumanized, and degraded," class history has said no.

In July, 1848, the socialist international held a congress in Hamburg. The name of Karl Marx was mentioned exactly once. The old slogans of the class struggle and exploitation had disappeared. But the words "liberty," "democracy," "human dignity" came up again and again. The leaders present at this socialist congress had participated in governments; they had learned to share power; but this had also taught them the limitations on the responsible use of power and on the responsible opposition to the party in power. Indeed, from one important angle, democracy may be defined as a sense of the proper rules of this game in which the party in power does not exterminate the opposition but makes responsible use of its power. The party in opposition does not completely discredit the party in power or the government and so avoids a chaotic situation; it uses its critical opposition responsibly. The principal theoretical speech of this socialist congress at Hamburg was made by Oscar Pollock. His theme was "The Disappointment of Achievement"; his problem was, "Why is it that we cannot get the working classes excited about socialism any longer?" The answer that Pollock gave is that their lot is so improved, in a way which would have been incredible to nineteenth-century Socialists of any variety, that they are no longer easily moved by the slogans of class struggle and socialism; the improved welfare of the working class has put the socialist party in a difficult position.

The state, too, has not been amenable to Marx's predictions and analyses. It was supposed to be "the executive committee" of the numerically dwindling capitalist class. But, instead, the state has been more and more democratized; workingmen have been enfranchised even on the Continent of Europe, and the activities of government have been made ever more subject to the labor vote, to the farm vote, to the vote of all the intermediate classes. Main Street, not Wall Street, is able to cast the greater number of votes.

Out of labor's influence on government, and out of the general pressure of society as a whole, have come many reforms which Marx thought impossible. There have come the state regulation of economic life, the legal limitation of the hours of labor, minimum wage, protection of health and conditions of labor, legalization of the right to organize, prohibition of the use of police and army against picket lines, institutionalization of collective bargaining, and a whole sweep of social-security legislation. As the French Socialist, Paul Deat, has summed up the process, it is "a socialization of power"; or as the German socialist thinker, Paul Lensch, put it, "The state has undergone a process of socialization while socialism has undergone a process of nationalization."

But even more startling than these changes is the series of economic novelties which have made the abstractions of the nineteenth-century economists (Marx and his opponents) totally obsolete as modes of generalization and understanding. These changes include protectionism, currency manipulation, deficit spending, price ceilings, price floors, state-fostered cartelization in many countries, antitrust prosecution, and, in vast areas of the world, autarky. Whether these features are to be welcomed or feared, they have produced a world which makes the projections of Marx and his opponents alike irrelevant to the modern scene.

The unkindest cut of all has been that the workingman has not consented to being increasingly proletarianized. Nor has he accepted the mission that Marx conferred upon him. He has displayed stubbornness, tirelessness, courage, skill, incapacity to recognize when he is licked, and the power to enlist the sympathy of much of society in fighting against this prophetic assignment. "It isn't a question," Marx wrote, "of what this or that proletarian, or even the entire proletariat, may for a time imagine to be its goal. It is a question of what the proletariat is, and what that being will historically force it to do." But unlike the declassed intellectuals who offered them leadership, the workers themselves have never been attracted to this mission. They have had no stomach for being reduced to nothing so that they may prepare themselves to become all. It is against this that their class struggle is directed; against this they have used their numbers, their solidarity, their influence on others, on other parts of society, even their competition, to become something in the world in which they have their being, not everything in a world which exists only in the fantasy of the utopians of which Marx was perhaps the greatest. It is to these aims that they have rallied, and to these aims modern society as a whole has rallied with them. In the words of the "International," "We have been nought, we shall be all"; but once they have become something the whole scheme loses its tidy outlines.

The secret of Marxism's power to survive the shipwreck of all its prophecies lies in its inherently dual character. On the one hand it claims to be a science. It claims to have made a science out of history, sociology, economics, politics, and to do for them what Darwin did for the biological sciences, indeed, to do even more: to explain the past and to make clear the present (as Darwin tried to do), and to foresee and control the future (as Darwin did not dare to do). But so badly has a century dealt with these claims that in the Western world where one is free to question, no Marxist intellectual now ventures to mediate between Marxism and the non-believer without a large measure of what the lawyers call "confession and avoidance." Indeed, when they are pressed, they are apt to discard one by one all the results arrived at by Marx's method and to insist only on the validity of the method itself. Thus we are confronted with a spectacle that would have astounded Bernstein and Kautsky alike.[1] Today, all "orthodox" Marxists *in partibus infidelium* are at the same time "revisionists," albeit reluctant ones.

If as a science, Marxism has been stripped down to a method which has produced only invalid results, Marxism's staying powers lie in the fact that it is also an ism. There is no Lockeism, no Smithism, no Millism, no Weberism, no Durkheimism, no Micheletism, no Rankeism, no Gibbonism, but there is a Marxism and this is significant. In the fact that Marxism is not a science, but primarily an ism, lies its power for mischief and fanaticism. It is an ideology in the precise sense in which Marx himself used the term. It is a creed that can be clung to by faith where the intellect questions and rebels.

When a faith is passionately held, no fact can refute it; it is charged with emotion and cannot be shaken by the mere refutation of any number of detailed matters; it is maintained by rationalizations and gives ground, yet resists; it is filled with the thunder of denunciation and sustained by a sense of righteousness and the assurance of prophesy. In an age prepared by two thousand years of Christianity in which the faith of millions had grown dim and the altar seemed vacant of its image, Marxism arose to offer a fresh vision of the last things, a new hope of the Apocalypse, a day of wrath when the mighty should be humbled and the lowly exalted, a new millennial kingdom of justice and freedom and happiness on earth, a world where life would lose its uncertainties and cease to play unexpected tricks upon men. History was to be given a new meaning, a new goal, and a new end in time—"the end of prehistory" is what Marx called it. There was to be a new integral faith and a providential certitude to guide man's uncertain steps and his faltering thoughts. The initiate were to be the new elect, armed with both understanding and vision; and the proletarian—the lowly and humbled, becoming ever more debased, outraged, and injured—was to be crucified, crowned with thorns, then armed with the vengeful lightning, to become, not only for his own class but for all mankind, the new

Redeemer. Then, at last, man would become as God, master of his own destiny, maker of his own future, conscious architect of his world. Moreover, he would become, if not omnipotent, at least omnicompetent, as that quotation from Marx proved which described him as fishing in the morning, hunting in the afternoon, and doing philosophical criticism in the evening without being a fisher, a hunter, or philosopher. The very division of labor which made possible the modern world was to be ended and man was to become whole.

Thus Marxism attracts because, as one Marxist, Henri de Man, once wrote of its attraction for him, it seems "as certain as science, and as integral as religion." Hebraic prophecy and Hebrew-Christian chiliastic expectations are combined with the worship of that Faustian demon of an earlier age which had become the fashionable deity of nineteenth-century worship, namely, science. The two powerful cults reinforce each other. According to the audience addressed, the Marxists of our day lean more heavily on the one or on the other.

Today, all neo-Marxists who must speak to those who are intellectually free are engaged in an enormous rescue operation. One branch seeks to rescue Marx's abstract model of the economy from the ravages of time. The other flees from the shipwrecked galleon of economic prophesy to the blessed isle of Marx's earlier utopian visions. The watchword of the one school is "Marx's method," and the watchword of the other is "Marx's humanism." They don't call it utopianism. In Marx's writing, since he is a cloudy and orphic writer, there is a Marx for any circle one approaches, for every changing fashion and mood. One has but to pick and choose. Marx is self-contradictory rather than systematic, and at his best a great stylist dealing with matters of deep human concern. His utterances have resonance and reverberate in such fashion

that even a few of them may go a great way. It is fatally
easy to find one's stock-in-trade—a little body of quotations
from the vast work—and enlarge it by repetition, contempla-
tion, and exegesis. Chipping thus a fragment from the huge,
roughhewn figure, the neo-Marxist proclaims, "Behold my
Marx." "Behold the real Marx."

For the other branch of neo-Marxists who would cling to
Marx the economist and scientist, the rescue operation consists of efforts to explain, or explain away, the treacherous
behavior of actual economic development by treating each
novelty of history as a deviation from the essential and the
lawful and that which is predetermined in the long run. An
effort is made to show that, though there may be shoals or
even dry land or mountain peaks where there was supposed
to be deep water, still the course the great pilot set was essentially right. Sly history's novelties do not make the old
road map useless; they merely represent long and explainable, if unexpected, detours. "When a theory shows itself
incapable of explaining or even describing reality," one
critic, Herbert Luthy, has written, "its believers set themselves to writing books where they explain why the theory
remains sound at bottom all the same, and wherein reality
has erred. Thus it is that pre-Keplerian astronomy hardened
into an impenetrable thicket of auxiliary hypotheses minutely elaborated, tables of deviations, squarings of the circle,
with the sole purpose of making room for the re-entry of the
incompatible results of new observations into the established
system of geocentric astronomy or into the circular orbits
of Copernicus."

The theoretical economists of the nineteenth century, and
Marx who was their disciple as well as their critic, worked
with an abstract model of the economy which, in part de-
liberately and in part unconsciously, abstracted from such

aberrations as state intervention and regulation, state fostering and restraining, nationalization, protectionism, currency manipulation, the influence of organized groups, legalized cartelization, legislated competition, enforcement by public or quasi-public bodies of quantities, qualities, price levels, import quotas and prohibitions, and the embryonic germs of the welfare state and of autarky. In other words, they abstracted from the political intervention of the state in the economy, which is precisely the characteristic phenomenon which has grown and spread until it overarches our age in the field of economics.

It is interesting that in Marx's day they spoke first of national economy; then of political economy; then after Marx, it became economics with the politics left out. And now it should be called economic policy, and in most languages "policy" and "politics" are the same word; for it is the social and governmental economic policy that is the basic determining factor in the modern world. Their world—that is, the world of the nineteenth-century classic economists, —was one of autonomous economic forces, with free movement of men, money, goods, and ideas. The intervention of all these extra-economic forces they treated as negligible or as having entered into a permanent decline with the end of mercantilism—and the growth of laissez faire. That abstract model might still have been a useful conceptual instrument for approaching the world of the first half of the nineteenth century. But with the manifest decline of laissez faire, theoretical economics went into an eclipse, since reality departed further and further from the models based on the free working of economic forces. Then came the age of the epigones, exegetes, and fragmentalists, men who worked on some fragmentary aspect such as statistical series, currency and budgetary manipulation, and the like. When a new synthesis came, or what passes for a synthesis in Keynes, it was precisely the question of governmental economic policy that was his concern. Marxism was painfully lacking in original thinkers after Marx's death, and classical economy was lacking in original thinkers during the same period.

Even when Marx was writing *Das Kapital*, it was already becoming clear that the public powers and organized groups were intervening in the raw or autonomous economic processes with ever greater scope and rigor to regulate their consequences and alter their direction. A large part of *Das Kapital* actually deals with the factory acts and the regulation of the length of the working day. Even when these efforts at regulation had, as they often did, consequences that were unintended, the autonomy of the economic process was nevertheless at an end.

Whether laissez faire is regarded as a blessing insuring eternal harmonies, as Bastiat would put it, or as a curse on industrial society leading it straight to the jungle of civil war, the abstract model, which was a useful and not too far-fetched conceptual fiction when his masters were writing, was already becoming useless and increasingly misleading when Marx began *Das Kapital*. Hence orthodox neo-Marxism has moved further and further from reality, has limited itself to expounding his doctrine as he left it, or to cite Luthy once more, "to making an exegesis of the history of the world insofar as it is a history of the deviations from the Marxist scheme." As Hayek and Roepke have sought to keep alive the vanished dream of the eternal harmonies of Bastiat, so Hilferding, Luxemburg, Lenin, Bukharin, and Sternberg have sought to keep alive the eternal disharmonies of the essentially identical dream world of Marx. The epigones of both schools still continue to feel at home in this world of abstract schemata, for only there can they theorize freely, and pleasantly abstract from both historical survivals and historical novelties, from all the extra-economic and non-economic factors that make the real world so complex, so unmanageable, so resistant, and so unpredictable. Actually, both schools live in a lost world, for what the later nineteenth century witnessed and the twentieth century has enormously accelerated is the total breakdown of the usefulness of the concept of autonomous economic laws and the total ship-wreck of all the predictions that Marx derived from the assumption of their autonomy.

1. Eduard Bernstein and Karl Kautsky were the two best known protagonists in the great battle over "Revisionism" in the first years of the twentieth century.

Leonard B. Schapiro

Marxism behind the Iron Curtain

T HE STORY of Marxism behind the Iron Curtain must, of course, begin with an examination of the way in which the thought of Marx was received in Russia in the nineteenth century. It is not enough, I think, to start from the point where Marxism in the hands of Lenin becomes an enormously potent force. Marxism was, in fact, first adopted in the sixties by the populists, the Narodniki. The populists did not believe in a future proletarian revolution or in any process of inevitable development from capitalism to socialism, but believed, in fact, that it would not be necessary for Russia to go through the capitalist stage; certainly, they profoundly hoped that it would not be necessary.

There were two reasons why Marx's influence was so strong among the populists. First, the populists welcomed Marx's condemnation of the evils of capitalism (and especially in Marx's dramatic terms) because they were hoping to avoid that kind of fate for Russia. Secondly, they also thought (and with some justification) that Marx shared their optimism in believing that it would not be necessary for Russia to pass through capitalism, and that it could go straight to socialism. Let us look for a moment at Marx's views—we have, for example, in 1882, the Preface by Marx (and Engels) to the Russian edition of the *Communist Manifesto* in which he said this: "If the Russian revolution becomes the signal for a proletarian revolution in the West, so that each complements the other, the present Russian common ownership of land may serve as the starting point of a communist revolution." In the previous year he had, as a matter of fact, belabored "those gentlemen who were opposed to revolutionary activity and were preparing for the leap, all in one, into the anarchist, communist, atheist millennium by means of the dullest of dull doctrinaire views." Who were those gentlemen? Primarily, Marx was referring to Plekhanov, who went abroad to Geneva and Zurich in order to avoid the police in Russia, thus exasperating Marx who, perhaps, didn't know all the facts of the situation. For Marx really wanted them to stay behind and do their best to blow up this horrible regime, the fated fall of which he regarded as the matter of prime consequence. Plekhanov, however, laid the foundations of social democracy in Russia in 1883, during his exile.

The reason why Marx was, perhaps, more acceptable to the populists was that he disclaimed any attempt to transform his theory of the development of capitalism in western Europe into a theory generally applicable to all countries, or as he put it, "to transform my historical sketch of the genesis of capitalism in western Europe into an historical-philosophical theory of a universal movement necessarily imposed by fate upon every people whatever the historic circumstances in which it finds itself. . . ." That was in 1877. Now Engels in 1875, in polemics against someone who could perhaps be described as a precursor of Lenin, Tkachev, got nearer than Marx to realizing that the social structure of Russia resembled much more closely what might be called the arbitrary despotism of an Oriental, Eastern society than the institutionalized legal order which in western Europe had emerged as the result of feudalism—an order which had never existed in Russia. The picture in Russia until 1861 was one of centralized, arbitrary bureaucratic control, headed by an autocratic power unlimited by law, which zealously prevented the emergence of independent institutions except when very carefully safeguarded and controlled by completely dependent officials—including the landlords whom Nicholas I had once described as "my unpaid police chiefs."

Even after 1861, when the peasants were liberated, this social situation never wholly disappeared. An attempt to create a social foundation for constitutional government in Russia was made only after 1906, and then the war came and it was much too late. This background of Russian history is, I think, vital in understanding why it was that Marxism, or Marxism in the form in which it triumphed, conquered when it did. Peter Struve, who was one of the earliest exponents of Marxism in Russia, drew the inference early in 1894, in his *Critical Remarks on the Question of the Economic Development of Russia,* that if any attempt were made to circumvent or cut short the full development of capitalism and institutions on the Western model in Russia before any question of a socialist order could arise in Russia, the only result would be a return to serfdom. In other words, if the institutions were not permitted to develop, if power were merely seized while the institutional structure still retained many of the characteristics inherited from the arbitrary government under serfdom, the result would only be another form of despotism and serfdom.

Now Struve was the leading so-called Legal Marxist in Russia. He belongs to what might be called the second reception of Marxism in Russia, not by the populists but by people who already called themselves Marxists. The Legal

Marxists, and indeed most Russian Marxists until Lenin, to some degree accepted the doctrines of Marx as a hope for the distant future rather than as a plan for action. They accepted his analysis as ultimately applicable to Russia, but only after a very long phase in which capitalism developed along Western lines; and they believed that although this would mean a great deal of misery, it would also bring with it the development of free institutions, civil and political freedom, and the rest. This view, of course, cannot be described as very revolutionary because in practice it meant that others (the bourgeoisie) would have to bring about the first revolution; the task of carrying out and advancing the first or bourgeois revolution would lie in the hands of the bourgeoisie themselves. While this doctrine may have corresponded to the views of Engels and to Struve's condemnation of premature attempts at short cuts to Utopia because it presupposed the development of capitalism and capitalistic institutions, I think it is also easy to see that a great deal of patience was needed to swallow that view if one hoped to see a revolution in one's own lifetime. For at the turn of the century in Russia, the proletariat numbered at most two and a half million, possibly less. The country was still an agricultural one even though industry was fast developing. Yet, according to Marx, the socialist revolution could only come about after the proletariat became the great majority.

As a slight palliative to this view, Akselrod and Plekhanov worked out what they called the "theory of hegemony," which was the theory that the proletariat would have to lead the bourgeois parties. When the bourgeois parties developed, they would be so cowardly—so much more cowardly, according to the Manifesto of the First Social Democratic Party Congress in 1898, than the bourgeoisie were in the West in asserting any kind of rights—that it would be necessary for the proletariat, the workers, to seize hold of them, lead them, and keep them on the true traditional, true historic revolutionary path. It was not a very practical doctrine. When bourgeois parties appeared, it became quite obvious that they were not going to be led by the Social Democrats or the proletariat and that they had ideas of their own. The doctrine of hegemony was very quietly dropped. This was the second reception of Marxism, the first by Social Democrats but the second reception in Russia.

We come to Lenin and the third reception of Marxism in Russia. The radical alterations which Lenin made in the ideas of Marx are fairly well known, and I shall only summarize them in three simple propositions. First, the proletariat lacks revolutionary consciousness. Unless this is brought to it from the outside, it will fritter away its energies on ephemeral material demands and will never do the one thing it ought to do in its own interests—make a revolution. Secondly, the making of the socialist revolution cannot be left to history and to the proletariat as a class unless there is maintained a professional, disciplined party of revolutionaries who will lead the proletariat along the right lines at the right moment. Thirdly, there exists at every historical moment a scientific, true course. Once this true course is discovered by the proletariat through its vanguard, the party, there should be no room for discussion; the true view should be substituted for the false.

Now I think Lenin's opponents at the time were right in maintaining that none of these propositions was discernible in the doctrines propounded by Marx and Engels. At best, I suppose it can be argued that the idea of scientifically discoverable truth does exist in Marx; it is, indeed, a part of the general, rational heritage of the nineteenth century. In Lenin's hands, however, this was transformed by the intro-

duction of the party, the vanguard, as the sole repository of
the higher wisdom. For the process of scientific inquiry was
substituted a kind of self-appointed priesthood which would
decide what was right. One could add to this Lenin's strong
emphasis on the need for discipline in the party, an emphasis
that was partly the result of Lenin's own character and partly
the result of the conditions in which a social democratic
party had to work in Russia before the revolution. But I am
afraid that it soon became clear that the repository of scientific truth meant Lenin; and that was simple enough because he had his very great moral authority. After Lenin,
the repository of scientific truth, absolute scientific truth,
became Stalin, who did not have the moral authority but
who had an excellent police force—and that seemed just as
good.

Lenin's opponents, the Mensheviks, argued that Lenin's
views were inconsistent with Marxism. Although these opponents produced admirable theoretical writings in the years
before the revolution, they were not very good tacticians if
only because they lacked the strength of character to put their
theories into practice. If you believed—as many Mensheviks
did believe—that what Marx was saying was that there would
have to be a long period in which capitalism, with all its
horrible as well as beneficent effects, developed in Russia,
and that eventually, at the end of that long period and with
the institutional basis which capitalism had created, there
would be a social revolution; if you believed this and you
were a Social Democrat, then logically what you ought to
do was to help the middle-class parties, the bourgeois parties,
to build up that structure while capitalism was developing,
and then wait for the fullness of time when one day your
grandchildren or great-great-grandchildren would lead the
proletarian revolution. Actually, they were not quite so con-

sistent, and I think it is not very difficult to understand why. Since they were not consistent, they concentrated almost as much as Lenin and his supporters on quick returns, on the speeding up of the revolutionary process. They also did their best, in a sense, to bring about reunification with Lenin and his supporters; at least they made the effort. But you cannot reunite with somebody who does not want to unite with you. As a result, the Mensheviks always offered something a little like the bolshevik theories but a little less radical, a little less revolutionary; and so, of course, they lost completely, and may, in fact, be said to have played into Lenin's hands, in spite of the great intellectual qualities behind many of their works. As I said, some of the best Marxist writing in the history of Russian intellectual thought came from the pens of menshevik opponents of Lenin during the period after the revolution of 1905, when open publication on political matters became more or less possible. But that's about all. Nobody reads those writings now, inside Russia at any rate. They may be said to have left no influence at all, so far as I am aware, on the subsequent development of Marxism (if such it can be called) in Russia. Strictly speaking, the history of Marxism in Russia virtually comes to an end with the victory of Lenin in 1917; because, whatever you may call it, you can't really saddle Marx with the October Revolution, that seizure of power in which a more or less popular and in form democratic government was overthrown by a carefully organized conspiracy in a largely agricultural country in which capitalism had only just begun to develop. I think it is not really possible to reconcile this with anything that Marx wrote about. Strictly speaking, then, the history of Marxism in Russia may be said to end with October, 1917.

On the other hand, the doctrines that have been developed inside Russia for the last forty-two years do pass for Marx-

ism, in the sense that many people believe that they are
Marxism; indeed, I have no doubt that many Russians believe they are founded upon Marxism and are closely connected with it. Since what people think is often of greater
importance in history than facts, it is legitimate, I believe,
to continue to discuss the development of Marxism in Russia,
even after October, 1917, if you put quotation marks around
the word. I think it would be very dull, however, if I tried
to go through all the strategems, all the ingenuities by which
Lenin and Stalin, and even Stalin's successor, have tried
to reconcile their tactical maneuvers with the works of Marx
and Engels, or such of their works as are still available to
people in the Soviet Union. But without undue cynicism, we
may say that Lenin and Stalin were here not strictly concerned with the realm of thought. If they could not convince
their opponents, they could always insure the triumph of a
particular view at a particular time by the administrative
elimination of their critics (which is interesting as a form
of politics, but has nothing to do with ideology). However,
it is worth while to consider certain key moments in the
development of doctrine in Russia because they reveal some
of the characteristics—one in particular—which, I suggest,
are the most interesting development of Marxism in the
Soviet Union today.

The first key moment is the development of the principle
that party supremacy must always come first—"principle,"
be it noted, not "practice." There was never any doubt in
Lenin's mind so far as practice was concerned, but I speak
now of principle in the sense of a theoretically formulated
doctrine. This development took place around 1921, at the
end of the Civil War, when the Bolsheviks faced a challenge
to their right to rule the country on their own, not only from
the whole peasantry, but virtually, I should say, from the

whole proletariat or a very large percentage of it. The seizure of power by the Bolsheviks in 1917 was theoretically a proletarian revolution, not a bourgeois revolution, and the ensuing regime, in accordance with Marx, was described as a "dictatorship of the proletariat." The Mensheviks had, I suppose, driven another nail into their own coffin in 1918 when they recognized that the October Revolution had been a historical necessity. Well, if the October Revolution was a historical necessity, then, according to their own theory, they themselves ceased to have any further historical justification. Yet in 1921, when the New Economic Policy was adopted, all this was reversed. The period of war-communism of the preceding three years was now described as premature, as a mistake; and it was recognized that private property and private enterprise would have to exist for a considerable period—as Lenin put it, for generations but not for centuries. In one of the very last things he wrote, Lenin argued that all previous attempts to introduce communism had been a mistake since the country was a backward peasant country, and that the hope for the future lay in the maintenance of some form of state socialism which would ultimately lead to the conversion of the peasants to the merits of co-operative association. In one sense this was an admission that Lenin had stood Marxism on its head, had changed it from a social process in which the production relations determined the state structure into one in which the state structure determined production relations. It illustrated, I think, that Marxism had in fact become a political method of industrializing backward countries in which the absence of free institutions made the continuance of state dictatorship the only way of accomplishing such a difficult task— a condition, in fact, rather like the one that Struve had foreseen in prophesying the return to serfdom, the continua-

tion of the bureaucratic, despotic method of government
from above. The consequence of this assertion of the primacy
of politics over economics was soon apparent in practice;
for if the view of Marxism required that in correspondence
with the bourgeois-capitalist base there should also be a
bourgeois-capitalist superstructure (that is to say, a parliamentary political machine), Lenin, by finally eliminating
from the scene all of his socialist and quite a number of his
communist opponents in 1921, showed where the real primacy lay. In all the vagaries of subsequent communist doctrine, this political primacy has never in one single instance,
so far as I am aware, been officially questioned.

The second key period is from 1921 to 1934. It is a remarkable period in that it revealed the extent to which the
acceptance of bolshevism had been an act of faith and not
an act of reason. In other words, the emotional impatience
with the rational interpretations of Marx—the long period
of waiting that was involved until capitalism had run its full
course, and the moment of revolution had arrived—the emotional impatience with the rational interpretation of Marx
propounded by Struve and by some of the Mensheviks, was
more at the root of bolshevism than any logical or scientific
reasoning. They believed in bolshevism because they wanted
to believe in revolution. Therefore, when bolshevism brought
with it none of the things that it had promised, they could
only retain their faith in it by further acts of faith and not
by reason. This becomes apparent when one looks at the attitude of many of those who opposed Stalin in the period
from 1921 to 1934.

Surprise has sometimes been expressed that Stalin ever
managed to remain in power in the face of so much influential opposition at a crucial moment. The principal reason that he was able to defeat his opponents, apart from

terror and police and all the rest, was the existence of a certain ambivalence in their attitude. They realized that Stalin's regime had become much more a bureaucratic despotism than a workers' state. They also realized that much of Stalin's political formulation—socialism in one country, for example, or the justification of the rapid and forceable collectivization of the peasants—bore no relationship to the views of Lenin and still less to those of Marx. They also realized that if they were to make a determined effort to overthrow Stalin's regime, they would unavoidably endanger the survival of any kind of bolshevik rule; and so their opposition remained half-hearted and never determined enough really to succeed. I have often had the impression in reading their speeches—on occasions when such opposition speeches were still permitted in the twenties and very early thirties—that these people knew that they were merely talking in the air; that no practical result was going to be achieved; that the majorities were packed against them; that the ruffians who were going to shout them down were already in position. The whole thing was a form of play acting, and they seemed on many occasions to realize it, and on one or two occasions actually said so. Since their fear of counter-revolution, as they would have described it, inhibited their actions, it was perhaps not altogether surprising that they should have been forced to rationalize, to dramatize their sense of impotence in what, I think, was a quasi-religious form. And in the quasi-religion, or pseudoreligion, of these oppositionists, "history" is the largest single element, history in the abstract. For them history became something akin to a substitute for God in the traditional religion. Just as the religious believer seeks consolation for injustice in the life to come, so the disillusioned Bolshevik sought consolation in the faith that what he himself was impotent to achieve would, in the end, be worked out to the right conclusion by history. Just as the traditional believer seeks to reconcile events and happenings which do not make sense in terms of human justice by recourse to a divine justice of which he is not able to perceive the totality but in which the irreconcilables are reconciled, so the disillusioned Bolshevik sought such a reconciliation in a similarly abstract superhuman force, namely history.

To support the view I have ventured to put forth, permit me to offer two illustrations of how oppositionists reacted, faced as they were with certain defeat and without any hope of having their views accepted.

The mystery about Trotsky that has puzzled so many people is that he could quite easily have defeated Stalin in 1923. He had Lenin's authority behind him. He had a great deal of following in the party. Stalin as yet had little following and had not built up the great apparatus that he used to defeat Trotsky. Why did Trotsky do nothing about it? When it was too late, after the party machine had already been perfected, why did he make a number of desperate moves which could only end in defeat and disaster, and which in any case he would soon have to recant? I think the answer is already to be found in the ambivalence which is apparent in 1924, at the Thirteenth Party Congress. When he was faced with the demand that he not only submit to party discipline but also recant his views (the first time that had happened in the history of the party), he agreed to submit to party discipline but he refused to recant. This is the way he gave his reasons:

> Comrades, none of us wishes to be or can be right against the party. In the last instance the party is always right because it is the only historic instrument which the working class possesses for the solution of its fundamental tasks. I have already said that nothing would be easier than to say

before the party that all these . . . declarations, warnings, protests were mistaken from beginning to end. I cannot say so, however, because, Comrades, I do not think so. I know that one ought not to be right against the party. One can be right only with the party and through the party, because history has not created any other way for the realization of one's rightness. The English have a saying, "My country right or wrong." With much greater justification we can say, "My party right or wrong, wrong on certain partial, specific issues, or at a certain moment. . . ."

No one knew better than Trotsky that this abstraction, the party, was by that time (1924) already under the control of a hand-picked bureaucratic elite which Stalin controlled. Indeed, the dying Lenin had warned Trotsky of something like this. I think that this mystique of the party as the instrument chosen by history for working out her hidden designs— the very quality of faith, the very quality of incantation about it—was what attracted Trotsky. Because it was absurd, in a sense, he wanted to believe it—*Credo quia absurdum*, perhaps, in a modern form.

Many years later, in exile, when he was reflecting on his defeat, Trotsky argued that only superficial minds would see the struggle between him and Stalin as a power struggle. Personalities, the greater skill of Stalin, he says, these things are quite irrelevant. What had happened? The struggle was a social process in which the bureaucracy had triumphed over the masses. Implicit in this argument was the assumption that if you bring the masses into the party all will be well again and Marx's principles will triumph. That is of some interest because it is a familiar argument today that if the masses can be brought back into the party (and in some cases it is said that the masses have indeed been brought back into the party), all the difficulties and unpleasantnesses in the Soviet Union, the aberrations in the thirties, forties, and fifties, will fall into perspective as part of a historic process. Stalin's reign of terror will be seen as a kind of industrial revolution which one must view as one large process. The faults of his policy then became mere aberrations in a particular stage of that process and not any inherent defect in the system.

I shall not enter into this particular argument, nor shall I discuss whether there is any truth in the suggestion that the "masses" have been brought back into the party today, either in Russia or, as is sometimes asserted, in Yugoslavia. My point is that whether or not the masses have been brought back into the party, we are not, in any case, anywhere near Marx's analysis. We are dealing already with something that started off in a different way. We are dealing with a despotic imposition of a bureaucratic government from the top, which may or may not be a good thing, and which is in many respects, obviously, quite efficient. That is not the point. What I say is that it bears little relationship to the particular form of social process discussed by Marx in which, after a long period of westernization and the development of capitalism, particular institutions would develop.

Let us take the rather more striking case of Pyatakov. Pyatakov was not a Jew; he was a Russian, of minor nobility. I mention this because there are many people who take the view, I think quite erroneously, that this chiliastic, messianic view of history among Russian Marxists is peculiar to Russian Jews because they have some kind of messianic instincts which other Russians do not. Pyatakov had been to some extent opposed to the New Economic Policy and, like Trotsky, had been an advocate of industrialization; he had been a Trotskyite, had signed the oppositional documents and had been expelled in 1927. Unlike Trotsky, however, he had recanted almost immediately, within a matter of weeks, and was readmitted to the party and appointed Soviet trade representative in Paris in 1928. In that year, in Paris, he was visited by a Social Democrat who had left the party in 1904, who had worked in the early twenties under him, together with many former Mensheviks, in the Supreme Economic Council for many years, and who knew him well. This man, Valentinov (or Vol'skii), who is now an old man but a man of very clear memory, saw Pyatakov, and in the course of conversation Pyatakov in some way hinted that Valentinov was afraid or cowardly. Whereupon Valentinov, not unnaturally, taunted him in reply: "Well, if we are talking about cowardice, what about you, recanting your views within a few weeks because Stalin barked at you?", or words to that effect. He was then treated by Pyatakov to an enormous tirade which lasted for about three-quarters of an hour, of which the following is the gist:

The essential Lenin was not to be found in the creator of N.E.P. [New Economic Policy]. This was simply the act of a tired man. The real Lenin, the one whom you Mensheviks will never be able to understand, was the man who had the courage to make a proletarian revolution first, and then set about creating the objective conditions theoretically necessary for it afterward. What was the October Revolution, what indeed was the Communist Party, but a miracle? No Menshevik could ever understand what it meant to be a member of such a party. It is bounded by no laws. It is always extending the realm of the possible until nothing becomes impossible. Nothing whatever is inadmissible or unrealizable for it. For such a party a true Bolshevik will readily cast out of his mind ideas which he has held for years. A true Bolshevik has submerged his personality in the party to such an extent that he can make the necessary effort to break away from his own ideas and can honestly agree with the party. That is the test of the true Bolshevik. There could be no life for me outside the party. And in order to become one with this great party, I was ready to believe—not only to say, but to believe—that black was white and white was black if the party required it.

If that is a rational acceptance of Marxism, then the words cease to have any meaning.

Just a few words on the subsequent tragic history of Pyatakov. He returned to Russia where he played an enormous part in the building of the first five-year plan. I think he knew what was going to happen to him; he was eventually arrested and charged in the usual way as a wrecker, a traitor, and all the rest. He confessed and was put on trial, one of those show trials, and shot in 1937.

We have traveled a long way from Marx. But our excursus does show something of the way in which Stalin was able to utilize both the fears of general collapse and perhaps a certain mystical, semireligious, pseudoreligious form of self-consolation that disappointed Bolsheviks had evolved. It is scarcely possible even to discuss so-called theoretical questions in terms of Marxism when one deals with the period after Stalin carried out his third revolution and expanded totalitarian control of life to a degree hitherto unknown in history. Stalin's main contribution is to be sought in the way in which Marxism was resorted to for purposes of administrative control over the population.

Stalin was, perhaps, the first to discover the new political principle that it is not necessary, even if possible, for a dictator to control men's minds. What can and should be done by a totalitarian dictator is to insure control over what men say, to invent suitable orthodoxies for all sections of intellectual activity, and then to make the intellectuals repeat these orthodoxies. Above all, they must not be allowed to remain quiet, thinking dangerous thoughts, without discrediting themselves by repeating official absurdities. This pre-

vents the emergence of centers of real intellectual speculation, which are always dangerous to a dictator; it also makes
the task of informers and spies much easier since they know
at a glance what is orthodox and what is unorthodox. So a
kind of public display of intellectual gymnastics is developed. But the importance of this as a method of political
control should not be minimized; it was vital to Stalin, although it has precious little to do with ideas. It relied completely on the very irrationality of the propositions that he
put forward, and, of course, the more irrational they were,
the better; since the more absurd the statement forced upon
an intellectual, the more he despises himself as a real intellectual. Stalin, I think, understood this.

It is an elementary proposition of politics that the less
force you use, the more support you need, and the more
persuasion you must use. This, I think, has become reflected
in ideology since Stalin's death. If ideology under Stalin
was a kind of magic formula for the enforced public gym-
nastic display, I think that it is now beginning to acquire
certain forms which are intended to captivate the imagination of the population, or the thinking part of the population
which is able to be captivated. What is the formula being
used? This is the interesting thing. The formula is our old
friend history, history in the abstract; the party, of course,
but the party as the instrument of history, carrying out the
design and dictates of history, moving forward to the historically predestined triumph of communism all over the world.
That is the picture which is being presented nowadays, and to
an extent which did not exist, so far as I am aware, under
Stalin.

If you compare two party histories, the famous *Short
Course*—Stalin's masterpiece—and the one-volume history of
the party which appeared recently (rewritten presumably to

the taste of Khrushchev), you immediately note the contrast. The *Short Course* is really a magic story: the fairy prince strides through the forest (forest of history, if you like) with various obstacles arising—wicked men, wicked beasts, Trotskyites, Bukharinites, kulaks, "economists," revisionists —all kinds of bogeys and phantoms arise in the way. These are vanquished one after another by the shining fairy prince who is, at the beginning, Lenin, and later, Stalin.

Now the new history is different. It is the picture of abstract history unfolding itself as a kind of ineluctable process. There are, of course, setbacks. Now and again there are even aberrations; for example, by Stalin. Power went to his head, just for a short time; his services were great, but for a short time power went to his head, and he somehow continued to believe that the class struggle had to be accentuated even after socialism had been accomplished and the whole population of the country was unanimously behind the party. But that had nothing to do, of course, with the wrongness of the party. The party was right, and that is proved by the fact that the party is now putting right the wrongs that Stalin committed. So it is no good to say, as enemies of the party do, that this shows that the whole system is no good, even when you get little aberrations—incidentally, at a modest estimate, the loss of perhaps twenty million lives. And so it goes on, moving to its ultimate triumph, the triumph of communism all over the world. Now every Russian knows what that means. It means, in fact, triumph of Russian domination, or, I suppose, conceivably joint Russian and Chinese domination over the rest of the world. That is what triumph of communism can only mean after forty-three years of the kind of leadership that Russia has exercised wherever communism exists.

In many ways this is not an unattractive image to present

inside Russia. It has that mystique of history. It leaves the
future to atone for the past and for the present. It has a certain appeal to chauvinism because, after all, it is "we Russians" who are doing this. History has chosen "us Russians"
to dominate the world. That's a very nice feeling. It has certain elements which, if you set your sights far enough ahead,
can even convince you of the triumph of communism in Russia—the gradual rise of bolshevism in the face of attempts by
the allied powers to prevent it; the defeat of the Germans during World War II; the enormous advance of communism
after the war; the complete failure of the Western world to
prevent that advance; the diplomatic successes scored by the
Communists; sputniks; first to hit the moon; industrialization; rise of material conditions in spite of great difficulties.
All those things for which we would be inclined to give the
Russians considerable credit, either for skill or courage, all
achievements whether real or imaginary, are attributed to
history, and, accordingly, in this great vision of a forward
march, history is almost deified.

Those of us who might well doubt the validity of many of
the prophecies of Marx and who, therefore, if left solely to
reason, would be very poor Marxists indeed, may be captivated by this kind of historical deity and by this picture of
the future in which the roughness and unpleasantness of the
past and present will be ironed out.

Let us glance briefly at Marxism outside Russia but still
within the Iron Curtain. While the stirrings in these countries
are of great interest, the attempt to stand against the imposition of the all-embracing party's strait jacket is something which of itself I cannot regard as ideological. It is very
admirable. I admire enormously the courage of those who are
prepared to face the very serious consequences of their criticism. But when it is analyzed, their criticism amounts to

little more than some quite elementary assertion such as that
it is not necessary, in order to write a poem or a history book
or run a factory, to have an uneducated party official at your
elbow telling you what to do. This does not seem to me to be
a contribution to Marxism or to any other doctrine of a
magnitude which would justify treating it as a theory.

There is one poem which I shall include because I think
it epitomizes the kind of criticism that is being made behind
the Iron Curtain—some of which is of extraordinary poign-
ancy. The poem is reliably attributed to Berthold Brecht,
and was written shortly after the uprising in East Germany
on June 17, 1953. I quote from a translation which appeared
in the course of a series of articles in *Encounter* in June,
1959.[1]

> After the rising of the 17th June
> The Secretary of the Writers' Association
> Had leaflets distributed in Stalinallee
> In which you could read that the People
> Had lost the Government's confidence
> And could only win it back
> By redoubled efforts. If so, would it not
> Be simpler, if the Government
> Dissolved the People
> And elected another?

Well, it's witty. It requires some courage to distribute a poem
like that. The courage and the wit I admire; but I don't feel
that we are here faced, with any question of a new theory,
doctrine, or interpretation of Marxism.

I think that this force of history, this faith in history as a
force behind Marxism, is something that one should not
underestimate. The fact that it is irrational, that it is not
very much connected with Marx—although historicism is an
essential side of Marx, it is not historicism transferred to

the party—is perhaps the essential feature of this modern historicism because the mystique of the party and the mystique of history are one and the same. It is only the party which is able to hear this voice of history, the "church" which is able to hear it and guide the faithful along the right path toward their destiny. This religious, quasi-religious, pseudoreligious (because, of course, it is fundamentally materialistic and therefore, I suppose, not properly to be described as religious) faith in history, in the destiny of Russia, in the rightness of the cause, must act as a sustaining and encouraging force, and, as such, I think it would be very unwise indeed to underestimate it.

Let me sum up in three sentences what I have tried to suggest are the strength and weakness of Marxism behind the Iron Curtain today. Marxism has been shaken by events and was, in any case, never intended to apply to Russia. Communism, in practice, has been discredited both inside and outside Russia by the bloody inhumanities that have been committed in its name. But history, as a faith, as an abstract faith, has in many instances replaced communism for those who still cling to belief in the ultimate rightness of the Russian bolshevik revolution.

1. Used by the permission of the editors of *Encounter* magazine and Martin Esslin.

Joseph Kerman

Debts Paid and Debts Neglected

WHEN WAGNER died in 1883, he left, as everyone does, full memories to his friends and to his enemies. His great legacy to the European consciousness was an ideology, and to the world of music a polarization, an alignment on either side of a split forced by confrontation with his scores. More tangibly, he left operas, music dramas, and a set of *Gesammelte Schriften* running to ten gold-embossed volumes in the second edition, revised and augmented by the author. Wagner left, inevitably, debts, which (again inevitably) were to be taken care of by somebody else. The question I wish to raise is: To what extent are we still paying off these debts? For, of course, over the years we have had to pay, and we have had to reckon in everything: *Das Judenthum in der Musik* as well as *Tristan und Isolde*, the split as well as the *Gesamtkunstwerk*, the dross of Wagnerism as well as whatever metal may be in Wagner's art.

By 1961, the friends and enemies have all been depersonalized into history—an obvious point, perhaps, but one that is worth noting. For so long as they lived, they extracted bitter interest in every transaction concerning the great man. Wagner was, to put it shortly, something of a monster in private life; and since that private life was well broadcast, the Victorians could not consider any aspect of the Wagner complex without considering the moral man. This is not the place to debate how, if at all, such consideration should weigh with a modern historian or critic. I note simply that as vivid personal memories fade, Wagner's conduct can take its place in our customary uncomfortable historical perspective, along with that of Tasso, Caravaggio, Rousseau, and other unpleasant great men.

The ideology of Wagnerism is now also essentially a matter of history, but it is a history that must detain us. The very term gives pause; word-forms of this order are rather rare and suspect, especially so within the arts. There are no such isms as Bachism or Mozartism or Schoenbergism, but there are Wagnerism, Orphism, Petrarchism, Darwinism, Marxism: all denoting frames of mind that go far beyond personal influence or personal propaganda, far beyond the strictly artistic, scientific, or social-scientific into the ideological realm. As soon as ideology begins by its very nature to transcend the local realities of the originating figure, it attracts the suspicion of professionals—musicians, scientists, or social scientists who see the fatal distorting appeal made in one direction to the dilettante, and in another direction to the mass. So as Wagnerism moved beyond music it moved with a good deal of hostility from the trade. And, paradoxically, although Wagnerism had begun with an idea about art, one did not need to be a musician to be a Wagnerian. The ideology could flourish divested of any essential artistic import.

If, as may happen, an ism were to grow up around a man posthumously or during his lifetime but without his active interest, it might possibly be passed over as irrelevant to his actual contribution. But of course this was not so with Wagnerism. The apologists are wrong when they claim that the ideology was manufactured only after Wagner's death,

in the unscrupulous Bayreuth press mill run by Cosima
Wagner, Houston Stewart Chamberlain, Glasenapp, Wolzo-
gen, and the rest. Wagner invented Wagnerism, fostered it
with the greatest care, and was for some years the first and
only Wagnerian. Moreover—and this touches at once the
fundamental artistic problem—Wagner has always been
suspected of caring more about Wagnerism than about art,
of writing his music dramas less as works of art than as
evidence for Wagnerism. If there is any truth at all in this,
it follows (paradoxically again) that we have to know
Wagnerism before we can know Wagner. Or looking at it the
other way, if there is no truth here, but only prejudice, we
have to know Wagnerism in order to confront the prejudice.
In any case, the debt to Wagnerism must be retired before
we can begin collecting royalties on Wagner's art. Examination of the ideology, then, is important not only per se
as a study of European culture of the last hundred years,
but also as a step to an appreciation of Wagner as artist. The
latter side of the question, of course, is the one that concerns
the critic.

Wagner's whole career may be scanned from the standpoint
of his development of Wagnerism. He first attracted mild
attention in the 1840's, a provincial conductor and composer
of operas in which such careful observers as Spohr, Liszt,
and Hanslick already appreciated qualities of restless
novelty. Actually, though the world was not yet loudly informed of the fact, Wagner was growing increasingly dis-
satisfied with the artistic situation as he knew it, and with
the state of society as a whole. This dissatisfaction, symbolized by great debts, made him eagerly join Bakunin in
the Dresden aftermath of the 1848 revolution, and partici-
pate actively enough to make it necessary for him to flee to
Switzerland. Thus more than he could ever have wished,

Wagner found himself forced into a quixotic rupture with society, a break that he was hardy enough to turn into a heroic, pathetic—but in any case prominent—stance. Exile also interrupted Wagner's career as a musician. Instead, he wrote voluminously for several years: tracts, pamphlets, polemics, treatises, and hundreds of letters in which ideas that had been in his head for some time settled into Wagnerism.

That this ideology, Wagnerism, absorbed into itself much of the thought of the time is a commonplace; obviously it did, or it could not have succeeded so well. It may even be true that every important element of Wagnerism had been enunciated separately before Wagner. His role was to make a brilliant synthetic formulation, and this is perhaps most simply approached not from its origins in intellectual history, but from the rather practical standpoint taken by Wagner himself. Wagner was first an artist. Basic to his thought was a special high calling for art, a high calling that may be succinctly characterized as "magical."

R. G. Collingwood makes much of this term in his *Principles of Art*. A "magical art," as he defines it, "evokes of set purpose some emotions rather than others in order to discharge them into the affairs of practical life." Magical art is to be distinguished from "entertainment art" which evokes emotions simply to gratify the audience, and from "art proper" which does not set out to *evoke* emotion at all but instead to *express* emotion. Under magical we can readily group medieval art, religious art, patriotic art, and such various low-brow arts as weddings, balls, banquets, and so on. Even low-brow magical arts have an urgency in society that Wagner coveted; and as for the high-brow ones, he dreamed avidly of their dignity or dominance in the world of affairs. Greek drama was Wagner's favorite archetype, a festivity expressing not any personal vision but the very life-soul of the city-state, and channeling the powers of feeling to the common good. Had not Plato insisted that certain modes of music produce virtue, while others should be banished from the republic? "Art as expression," in Collingwood's sense, was altogether too private a concept for Wagner's aesthetic, as was Hanslick's notion of music as *tönend bewegte Formen.* "Art as entertainment," however, Wagner knew well and reviled, and "Art as magic," on the highest of high-brow levels and with Wagner as the grand wizard, was his ideal.

A basic commitment to magic is naturally a basic commitment to unreason. In best romantic tradition, Wagnerism always claimed that music drama appealed to instinct rather than to reason. Many of Wagner's techniques bear this out, such as his opulent harmonic and orchestral sound and his use of repetition sometimes to a soporific degree. "Don't argue, repeat" might stand as Wagner's motto both in prose and in tone—the characteristic tactic of the demogogue. Considered as a group, furthermore, the heroes of Wagner's mature works provide an exhaustive study of unintellectuality in all its subtle shades: Siegfried the joyful savage, Parsifal the pure fool, Tristan whose intensity of will transcends law and life, Walther the spontaneous singer inspired by nature's birds and by the eternal Eve. (Walther does have his *Doppelgänger* to teach him form in addition to content. But even Sachs says of Walther's song: "Ich fühl's, und kann's nicht versteh'n"—which is enough for Sachs; as a good Wagnerian, he does his all for the hero.) Critical discrimination, on the other hand, was anathema to Wagner, and unscrupulously he pilloried criticism as pedantry and malice, making Beckmesser a personal caricature and a Jewish caricature for good measure. Wagner even opposed vivisection, an essentially analytical process which does indeed do violence to the *élan vital*.

But we are attempting to vivisect the ideology of magical art. In 1850, the ideal required two things: a new kind of art and something to be magical about. To a nineteenth-century German, the latter lay easily at hand in the gathering concept of the *Volk*, inchoate but free, impersonal but vital, true, and German. Thus Wagnerism plunged headlong into German *Kultur* mystique, with its corollaries of racial purity and anti-French sentiment. Art should discharge emotion to the purpose of driving the communal national consciousness along its dynamic march into the future. All this Wagner upheld emphatically, not only in the writings of his exile, but also later in the manual of statehood that he drew up for Ludwig II, *Was ist deutsch?*, and in the runic meditations of his last years. His *Gesammelte Schriften* formed a rich mine for later generations of mystic nationalists.

As for the former requisite, the new kind of art: Wagner invented this, and it remains one of the remarkable intellectual achievements of the century (in spite of his anti-intellectual stance, which was not without an element of sham, as we shall suggest later). Since Wagner's new art is to stir the *Volk*, it must reach a hitherto unreached audience. Only some sort of theater, with its well-known appeal and its well-known mystique, can serve—an idea already fundamental for Schiller, as Carlyle had observed. Since communion is achieved not by reason but by feeling, and since music is the art closest to unbound emotion, the new art must be some sort of musical theater. Not, of course, conventional opera—Franco-Jewish entertainment music at its most degenerate—but a new organic combination, a *Gesamtkunstwerk*. The idea of synthesis, so dear to the romantic spirit, guarantees a super-art combining the virtues of all: drama

served by music, poetry, gesture, and scene. The subjects
must stem from national myth, which presents eternal if
cryptic truths in ideal concentrated form. Since feeling, not
reason, can reach the *Volk*, once again, a whole new armory
of technical stratagems is required. Limitation of dramatic
"business," relentless piling up of repetitions, new breadth
of time-scale, a new steady pitch of intensity, *Stabreim*,
leitmotiv, orchestral continuity, transformation scenes, "endless melody," eight horns and four tubas—all these were
developed for the new magic.

Add to this the historistic dynamic interpreting this art as
the chosen art of the future, and add to it the organic fallacy
in aggravated form, and you have the main components
of Wagnerian ideology. The orthodox felt not only that each
Wagner music drama was a perfectly integrated work of art
in itself, but also that the seven of them formed a single
coherent corpus, sprung mystically from a basic seed. This
far, at least, the organic ideal holds good: irrationality and
Volk mystique cannot be dissociated from Wagner's concept
of art or from his highly individual artistic techniques. The
ideal of art as magic is comprehensible only in view of the
mystique; the techniques are comprehensible only in view of
the intended function of the art.

The entire structure, to repeat, was worked out in Wagner's
head after his exile in 1849. For six years he wrote no music
at all, but instead bombarded an astonished world with an
ideology that seemed to many dangerous visionary nonsense
—as did *Mein Kampf* in 1925. In 1853, however, Wagner
published privately the libretto for a gigantic *Gesamtkunstwerk*, *Der Ring des Nibelungen*, showing that he certainly
meant business; and it soon became known that he had composed the first two parts of the *Ring*, as well as (in 1859)
another mythical drama, *Tristan und Isolde*. Meanwhile, all

that one actually heard was his early music, which could be
pressed into the cause of Wagnerism only by means of out-
rageous special pleading. This was not lacking, and in 1860,
Brahms, then aged twenty-seven, felt constrained to sign an
unfortunate antimodernist manifesto, thereby formalizing
the corrosive rift in late nineteenth-century musical life. The
manifesto served to magnify the Wagner myth. So did two
famous fiascoes of this period: the 1861 Paris riots over
Tannhäuser and the retraction of *Tristan und Isolde* from its
intended première in Vienna after seventy-seven fruitless
rehearsals.

For years Wagner had little prospect for the performance
of his three extraordinary music dramas. Then, as is well
known, luck changed. The new king of Bavaria, though only
eighteen, was already a rabid Wagnerian, and under his aegis
Munich saw the first performances of *Tristan, Die Meistersinger, Das Rheingold,* and *Die Walküre* from 1865 to 1870.
Incredible as it seemed, Wagner had succeeded; and the nineteenth century was fairly hypnotized by this success. Fascinat-
ing also was Wagner's ruthless personal life: his success with
other men's wives, in his search for a mate who was also a
Wagnerian, symbolized mastery not only for Wagner but also
for his contemporaries—Siegfried the superman, after all, is
rewarded by Brünhilde. Wagner celebrated the War of 1870
quite unmystically by sending, unsolicited, a triumphant
Kaisermarsch to the Kaiser, and by circulating under a pseu-
donym and then actually publishing a wretched skit mocking
the fall of Paris, *Eine Kapitulation.* Wagnerism, he publicly
suggested, should become the official ideology of a resurgent
Germany now set on its historic mission. Bismarck was contemptuous, but Wagner had his way; and fifty years later,
Hitler was not contemptuous.

Wagner's way was the most formidable move in the history

of Wagnerism: Bayreuth. The time was right, with German nationalism at the height, with five Wagner music dramas newly before the public, and with the most impressive intellectual tribute to Wagner in the making: Nietzsche's first book, *Die Geburt der Tragödie aus dem Geiste der Musik.* In 1872, the cornerstone was laid for the Bayreuth Festival Theater, a temple specially constructed in a special idyllic Mecca for special celebratory performances of works specially to be created by the Meister. For the opening rite (1876) nothing less impressive would serve than the great tetralogy (or, to follow Wagner's anxious analogy with Greek drama, the great trilogy with an introduction) based on the myth of the German *Volk, Der Ring des Nibelungen.* As Bernard Shaw and others have pointed out, Wagner's final implementation of his twenty-year-old plan did more credit to his Wagnerism than to his artistic integrity. To make the next festival (1882) more awe-inspiring yet, art as magic was carried to its logical conclusion. *Parsifal*—a gigantic communion service, a static drama of priesthood—absorbs Christianity into Wagnerism as blandly as Arthurian romance had absorbed pagan grail rites into Christianity. *Parsifal,* too, looks back twenty years to *Tristan und Isolde* in a subtle, very interesting, and yet curiously reactionary way.

As the festivals at Bayreuth followed more frequently, their importance for the Wagner myth grew. Wagner had not only written, composed, fought, borrowed money, and stolen women—all prodigiously—but also he had *built;* and to the nineteenth century, the tangible symbol of the *Bühnenfestspielhaus* and the Villa *Wahnfried,* where Wagner's body rests, confirmed Wagner as the superman for whom it had yearned since Carlyle. That Bayreuth instantly became not an ideal, pure shrine but a somewhat vulgar commercial enterprise made no difference. This fact may have depressed

Wagner—though not deeply enough to hinder work on *Parsi-fal*—and it may have disgusted confirmed enemies like Nietz-sche, who now saw in Wagner every abomination of nine-teenth-century German culture. But confirmed friends, the pilgrim Wagnerians, the crowned heads, and the humble members of *Wagner-Vereine*—these responded not to the re-alization but to the ideal. Art had risen up and forced the world of affairs to make it a home and a temple. The artist was acknowledged legislator of mankind.

More than 10,000 articles and books had been written about Wagner by the time of his death, and the climax of Wagnerism was still to come. The 1880's saw the French Wagnerian movement, inspired essentially by Wagner's writ-ings (hard as that may be to believe today). Eduard Dujardin and Theodor Wyzewa of the *Revue Wagnerienne* were the standard bearers; Villiers de l'Isle-Adam and Mallarmé lent their authority; Catulle Mendès, Verlaine, Huysmans, René Ghil, and Maurice Barrès served as the younger contingent. What fired the symbolists was the Wagnerian cult of feeling rather than reason. For this they were prepared to ignore Ger-manism so thoroughly as to rationalize *Eine Kapitulation* as a parody on German glee at the fall of Paris; they were pre-pared to conclude that neither music nor the combination of arts was necessary to essential Wagnerism. Of such paradoxes any mystique is capable. In England, true-blue Wagnerians (the adjective is Ernest Newman's) were issuing a magazine with the highly unlikely title of *The Meister*. The late 1880's also produced Nietzsche's devastating critique. To counter this, the Bayreuth publicists found an even better tactic than their usual ones of ignoring, distorting, or villifying oppo-nents. Piously they commiserated with mad Nietzsche, and pressed him to their breasts as a brother Wagnerian on the basis of his early books.

The final, violent stage of Wagnerism was a political one, or perhaps we should employ the term coined by the Wagnerians themselves: a "metapolitical" one. For Peter Viereck, who developed this thesis in a furious book called *Metapolitics*, Wagnerism stands to nazi ideology as the most important single fountainhead. That a political leader liked to relax at the opera has in this case unusual and ominous significance: Hitler's well-known devotion to *Lohengrin* and *Siegfried* was not merely a matter of affection, like the late pope's affection for Bach, but a complete spiritual commitment. The line runs directly from the Bayreuth circle of Cosima Wagner and Houston Stewart Chamberlain to Alfred Rosenberg, Dietrich Eckart, and Adolf Hitler, who was introduced to Bayreuth in 1923. *Mein Kampf* is Wagnerian in style and content, and much later Hitler was to say, quite simply, that anyone who wishes to understand Nazi Germany must know Wagner. Much in Wagnerism the Nazis chose to ignore. But the nineteenth-century ideology provided soil and seed for all their key ideas: the communal spirit of the *Volk*, the relentless march into the future (*Lebensraum*), the goal of racial purity, the cult of might, the appeal to the irrational, the demagogic technique of "the big lie," and the mystic idea of the Führer.

This is not to say that Wagner could be claimed as a Nazi by retrospect, even if the Nazis did celebrate their victory at the polls in 1933 by a ceremonial performance of *Die Meistersinger*. They could not even make a nazi opera out of what is, in actual fact and in spite of what everybody says, not even a very nationalistic piece. However, they could manipulate it as symbol and as magic; and they were right in seeing the precursor of the Führer in the Wagnerian hero. By the same token, Beethoven could not be claimed as a Wagnerian, however frequently Wagner extolled and conducted the *Ninth*

Symphony to herald the Dresden uprising or to celebrate the laying of the cornerstone at Bayreuth. But again, the Wagnerians were right in seeing the precursor of Siegfried in Beethoven's ideal of the hero—if not perhaps in the "Eroica" Symphony, at least in the Schilleresque *Held* of the B-flat *alla marcia* in the *Ninth*. The romanticism of the early nineteenth century became Wagnerism in a later stage, and Wagnerism became the ideology of naziism, transcending the world of art altogether.

No further stage is evident. As was observed at the beginning of this long excursus, the ideology of Wagnerism is by now essentially a matter of history. The present has its own up-to-date mystiques, such as those of the Jungians and of the beat generation, but these can scarcely be traced to Bayreuth. Every once in a while, to be sure, we catch the true Wagnerian *Nachklang*. I caught it last year at a lecture by Karlheinz Stockhausen, as he explained how the music of instruments and human expression shall give way to the music of machines, and how a new concept of composition and a new type of concert hall shall come into existence—not *should* or *may* or even *will*, but *shall* according to an unnamed but all-compelling historistic necessity. Still, it was just an echo. This one of Wagner's debts has been squared, at the price of the nazi *Götterdämmerung*—or *Götzendämmerung*, Nietzsche would have said. And today, while Nietzsche remains in our intellectual heritage, Wagner seems to be in danger of becoming a forgotten man. Our debt *to* Wagner, that is to say, is for the most part neglected.

It was not always so. In the decades around 1900, when Wagnerism was a living issue, the tremendous artistic impact of Wagner's scores was likewise fresh and unavoidable. Only now have we allowed this impact to dim with time, wrongly I am sure. In those decades, indeed, Wagner as a composer was the main issue in the musical revolution dividing what is now called contemporary music from the nineteenth century. Half of the composers tried to encompass Wagner and carry through the implications of his work, while the other half tried to contradict him. Then as now, the terribly complex relationship between Wagner-as-composer and Wagnerism was a source of confusion, harassment, and depression. Yet, on the whole, Wagnerism *as ideology* had less influence in music than in certain other areas.

That is not strange: according to the musician's limited, professional, matter-of-fact way of looking at things, Wagner was simply another musician. Ideology commenced only as Wagner moved away from music. So while composers could be swept away by Wagner's technical innovations, they never quite cottoned to the ideology. For one thing, Bayreuth saw not the slightest need for a successor to the Meister. Richard Strauss, one musician who was able to take over Wagner lock stock and barrel and with amazing facility, turned the whole apparatus away from magic toward entertainment, so that in a certain sense he may be said to have betrayed Wagnerism more profoundly than anyone else. Scriabin, who would have added Indian mysticism, color, and scent to the already bulging *Gesamt* of Wagnerian orthodoxy, came to nothing. On the other hand, Bruckner and Hugo Wolf composed lasting symphonies and songs under the influence of certain of Wagner's techniques. So decisive, indeed, were these techniques at the historical juncture, that it was a follower of Wagner in this technical sense—not a follower of Brahms or Verdi or Rimsky-Korsakov—who became the key figure of the twentieth-century musical revolution.

Around Arnold Schoenberg and his school there still exists a split in musical life as jagged as that of Wagner's own time.

This item of the Wagner *Nachlass* has not been paid off; if anything, we appear to have taken on a heavy second mortgage. Is it the same split, or some kind of modified continuation of the old one, or something altogether fresh? The question is, I think, definitely worth pursuing. In the contemporary musical consciousness, the importance of the twelve-tone phenomenon and serialism would be hard to overemphasize.

Actually, two schools should be distinguished: the original Viennese twelve-tone group formed around Schoenberg and the recent international serial group formed around the memory of Anton Webern, Schoenberg's radical pupil. Between both of these schools and musical Wagnerism, striking parallels appear at once—on the surface at any rate: the same apparatus of composers, favorite conductors and performers always ready to present their work, devotees and hangers-on, intellectuals and publicists, magazines, societies, little festivals. Though the modern movement has always been much humbler in scope than Wagnerism, it has recently achieved a certain analogous chic. A little below the surface, the movements have in common the mode of polemic, the mood of an elite, and the adherence to a historicist view of musical progress. Like the Wagnerians, the serialists are marching along the one truly modern path, which has evolved inexorably from the past, in face of a reactionary opposition that is as powerful as it is underhanded. Equally scornful are the members of this opposition, armed with arguments very similar indeed to those of the anti-Wagnerians: twelve-tone music is too dissonant and chromatic for man or beast, too complicated, unsingable. It consists not exactly of "endless melody," but certainly of an endless unarticulated flux. The steady high level of intensity frays the nerves (Hanslick complained of "continuous nervous unrest" even in *Die Meister-*

singer). According to a somewhat more elegant criticism, twelve-tone music is feeble rhythmically (Nietzsche on Wagner: ". . . the complete degeneration of the feeling for rhythm, *chaos* in the place of rhythm . . ."). Below specific objections lies once again a blind conviction that the music is being composed less for its own sake than to justify an abstract, extra-musical system. What is more—and this turns the historicist argument back on itself—twelve-tone music is considered decadent on account of its roots. Wagner was accused of vulgarity *à la* Meyerbeer; Schoenberg is accused of tawdry romanticism *à la* Wagner. The twelve-tone school has to live with *Verklärte Nacht* and the Alban Berg *Sonata,* just as Wagnerism had to live with the prelude to the third act of *Lohengrin.*

Now even if there were no more connection than this, I should think it a matter of likely significance that the *form* of the Wagnerian quarrel is so clearly echoed in the twelve-tone quarrel—even if the *content* were not. This whole way of thinking about music was unknown before Wagner, or at any rate before Wagner crystallized the growing conflict in nineteenth-century music; though we take this way very much for granted today, it has its own peculiar modernity. However, the connection surely lies deeper than the form of controversy alone; and with all due care and with all due sympathy in both directions, I should like to examine analogies in content. As we have seen, the essence of Wagnerism was a partly extra-musical structure and a mystique. But is not the very same true of serial music? Obviously, the old structure and the old mystique differ enormously from the new ones in their actual natures. Equally obvious, to me, is the similarity between the two schools simply on the basis of their essential orientations around *a* structure and *a* mystique.

Structure for the Wagnerians was a relentless multiplica-

tion of musical, poetic, dramatic, philosophical, and ideological details to create the magical *Gesamtkunstwerk*. Structure for the original twelve-tone school was a systematic
application of a special method in composing a musical work
of art. Starting with what has been called his "precompositional assumption," the composer selects a set or row, a fixed
ordering of the twelve available notes of the scale. Then, as
raw material he uses pitches only in the sequence of the row
or of certain derivatives of the row (transposition, inversion,
retrograde, and combinations of these). From these origins,
the later serial school has developed methods requiring much
more complex operations on the row, and controlling musical
elements other than pitch—rhythm, timbre, dynamics, and
so on—by means of analogous "precompositional assump-
tions." To describe all this as structure will cause no difficulty, but to call a structure "extra-musical," or half–extra-
musical, which is so directly involved with the act of musical
composition, may appear mistaken and prejudicial. I grant
and stress that the term as used here means something quite
different from Wagnerian extra-musicality. Nevertheless, in
the very concept of the row, exhaustive and rigorous as it is;
in the frankly mathematical nature of the derivations and operations, notably with the latest serialists; and in the speculative quality of "precompositional assumption" itself—in
all these I think we can hardly fail to see something extra-
musical at work. That vaguely similar things can be seen in
some great composers of the past, too, in Josquin and Bach
and Mozart and Wagner, proves merely that extra-musical
ideas have been affecting great music for a long while.

What will cause more difficulty is reference to a twelve-
tone or serial mystique. The fact is that serialism is felt—
not thought, *felt*—to offer a key to the musically good. It
provides control by formula over the raw material of music;

it solves problems of logic and organization; and most important of all, it beards that great chimera of modern music, organicism. Indeed, the mystique is essentially one of organicism; to the most superficial twelve-tone sympathizers, application of mathematical technique guarantees an organic whole, which is to them tantamount to success. The fantastic apparatus of mathematical set theory and acoustical formulas, the shibboleth of "total organization," so-called—these belong to the most extreme new serialists, not to Webern or Schoenberg. Nevertheless, in a quieter form the idea of artistic success through increasingly rigorous control undoubtedly played its part with the original twelve-tone composers. The classic statement of this mystique has been made in artistic form in Thomas Mann's panoramic novel *Doctor Faustus*, whose hero is a mythical first twelve-tone composer. The modern Faust achieves a "break-through to the subjective"—an equivocal redemption—through a diabolic pact whereby he renounces humanity and even reason and suffers a cold bond to the mathematical and the occult in order to gain the strictest objective mastery over artistic resources. This excruciated dialectic Mann presents unforgettably, with the greatest imaginative penetration and sympathy. Mann was also able to see Wagner more steadily than most observers.

Schoenberg, however, publicly repudiated the book; with half of his strange being he fought against mystique, which is certainly more than can be said of our advanced serialists. To Schoenberg and his most intelligent sympathizers, serialism is just a technique, a "method of composing with the twelve notes," and true artistic problems come only after the "precompositional assumption" and all the manipulations of the rows. The historical "necessity" of Schoenberg's development is always insisted on. But the trouble with this non-mystical explanation is that serialism, viewed merely as a

working method, seems to everybody else artistically (if not
perhaps historically) arbitrary, imposed from the outside,
and, above all, labored. Why this method rather than another? Why the passion for rigorous application, which
could bring Schoenberg himself in his late years to incorpo-
rate dogmatic members of his row in unheard grace-note
chords? Conversely, what justification can be found for so-
called free twelve-tone composers—composers who are, as it
were, just a little bit pregnant? Viewed as a mystique, however, the twelve-tone system presents no problems at all. Number mystiques have nourished the arts since the time of Py-
thagoras, with good results as well as bad. It is certainly not
remarkable that in this scientific, uncertain age, musicians
and artists should seek a talisman.

Let there be no misunderstanding about the manifest differences between Wagnerism and serialism. The new mystique is
a compositional mystique, not a world view. The new structure is a technical structure, and even its extra-musical quality may be said to be technical rather than philosophical. The
twelve-tone and the serial schools eschew magic, demagogy,
aesthetic-politico-racial superstructure, and even personality.
The very names are not "Schoenbergism" but terms severely
expressive of technique; the literature comes in magazines
called not *The Meister, La Revue Wagnérienne, Bayreuther
Blätter,* but *The Score, Polyphonie, Die Reihe.* Most (not
all) of this literature is highly professional, beginning with
Schoenberg's written contribution, a *Harmonielehre*—and
Schoenberg was a great teacher, unlike Wagner and unlike
every other great composer since Bach. Personality is not the
issue here; if it were, we might reflect on the ironic, indeed
tragic, contrast between Wagner and Schoenberg in the out-
ward course of their careers, to say nothing of their conduct.
In serialism the Führer concept is totally absent, as irrele-

vant to a technical movement as it was essential to Wagner's all-embracing ideology. Consequently, serialism has more than one single master and is exerting a more profound, more flexible influence on the course of music than Wagnerism ever did, for all its pride in romantic dynamism.

All this is true; yet there is one more bond, and it is, of course, the deepest one, between Wagner and the twelve-tone system. In the historical moment, Schoenberg did not proceed illogically. He was meeting the great problem in musical style that was his debt inherited from Wagner—the problem stated emblematically in a famous book-title *Romantische Harmonik und ihre Krise in Wagners Tristan*, a study by Ernst Kurth (1920). Romantic music, seeking to mirror the inner life of feeling, had instinctively clouded clear forms wherever possible; most serious of all, it clouded the traditional framework of harmony and tonality. Seeking intense expressivity, romantic music leaned toward more and more chromaticism—a tendency that weakened the tonal system very specifically by drawing attention away from harmony and toward linear impulsion. All this came to a head in 1859 in the extraordinary score to *Tristan und Isolde*, which for most critics remains Wagner's finest work, as well as the most important musical work of the later nineteenth century. *Tristan* challenged the very postulates of music as it was known: the centrality of a tonic note, triad, or key; the accepted heirarchy of other notes, triads, or keys in relation to the tonic; the standard rhetoric of tendencies and relationships between one sound and another. For fifty years music hovered anxiously around this challenge, which Wagner took care to aggravate by many vexed, beautiful passages in his later operas. Schoenberg wrestled with musical organization first of all quite in Wagner's spirit; but as he followed through the implications of *Tristan*, the question of musical repetition, in particular, grew more and more problematic. Schoenberg's solution was to leave classical tonality altogether and to organize music in a radically different way. As a frame of reference for the "rightness" of sounds, he developed the serial principle, self-defined by a private "precompositional assumption" rather than accepted according to the tacit tradition of tonality.

The analogy with perspective may perhaps be helpful here. By Wagner's time, tonality as the fundamental binding force of music was thoroughly weakened under the stress of expressive linear chromaticism. Schoenberg's abandonment of tonality was as drastic a step as the abandonment of perspective in painting—as drastic and, some would say, as necessary.

It was obvious that Wagner had brought music to a breaking point. What caused the crisis, it is hardly necessary to add, was not simply the interest of his searching experiments, but rather the authority, that is to say, the integrity, of his operas as works of art. The situation was desperate enough; all serious composers in the early part of the century were trying to erect some kind of structure from the fallen bricks of classical tonality. That Schoenberg and Webern should have attempted a drastic solution is much less remarkable than the character of that solution: the rigid systematization with its strong leanings toward a mathematical mystique. The interesting fact is that analogues to this rigid systematization —the way they arranged the bricks—are already evident in the Wagner operas.

This seems a paradox; Wagnerism is dogged by paradox. What has Wagner's cult of irrationality and his endless, vague, emotional trance to do with a technique that has been accused of being cold and mathematical and which, it must be said, has never properly nullified the accusation? The paradox runs all through romanticism, starting before 1800

with Novalis's maxim of *Systemlösigkeit in ein System*—
"systemlessness as system." Seen from one side, this idea glo-
rifies irrationality. Seen from the other side, it sets up a system. And so it must be for the artist; romanticism might seek
to imitate life in its elusive, self-contradictory chaos, but the
artist if he wanted to do anything at all—whether to express
his soul or to influence others magically—had to come to a
point. Art has to assert form on content. Perhaps, indeed, the
more the artist wishes to give the impression of formlessness,
the firmer must he draw the secret bonds of artistic form. The
slice of life, the stream of consciousness, the impressionist
haze, and the expressionist nightmare are far from formless
in artistic realization. The paradox is evident in Maurice
Maeterlinck's *Pelléas et Mélisande*, for instance, a play dear
to musicians on account of the beautiful (and curiously Wagnerian) musical setting by a leading anti-Wagnerian, De-
bussy. The action appears to revolve around moody *non se-
quiturs* and aimless people drifting in and out; but just below
the surface lies the chromium grid of the well-made play. The
paradox comes in *Ulysses*, a dreamlike evocation organized
more minutely than any other major work of literature since
the *Divine Comedy*. It comes in Alban Berg's *Wozzeck*, whose
subject is crack-up, and whose form is an odd anthology of
tight purely musical structures.

In the music of the nineteenth century, it was Wagner who
reflected the paradox of Novalis most strongly. He worked
and schemed and plotted for his magic. The ancient Egyptian
priesthood is said to have made a great secret scientific dis-
covery, steam power, in order to rig miracles. A later age un-
masked them; and though Wagner's *Gesammelte Schriften*
are conspicuously silent on the subject of intellectual structures, these have become more and more apparent as analysts
vivisect the scores themselves.

Intellectual organization for Wagner was first a matter of leitmotiv structure, as was well understood at the time. The function of the leitmotiv is manifold: to work an elaborate cross-reference system for presumptive dramatic good, as well as to explain the action to an audience which is by design half-unmusical, but which as communing body must not be left in doubt. Another function is technical: as the musical continuity grows larger and more tenuous, the time-scale expands and tonality becomes more vague; therefore, it is urgent to have as many organizing themes as possible—to have plenty of foci, as it were, around which the fog can precipitate. Sometimes Wagner handled leitmotivs in a drab, mechanical way. With this in mind, Jacques Barzun interprets Wagner less as a romantic than as a "mechanist"; the insight is important, though the conclusion does not necessarily follow.

In addition to leitmotiv structure, Wagner used minute organization by phrase, period, and key; the "endless melody" is structured down to the bone. Guido Adler seems to have understood this first, around the turn of the century, and his ideas were exaggerated in the Wagner analyses of Alfred Lorenz, which are notorious in musicology as the *locus classicus* for Procrustean lopping. Nevertheless, although half of what Lorenz saw in Wagner existed only on his own drawing board, the other half was true, important, and something of a revelation. For instance, it had often been said that in spite of his claim to be following Beethoven, Wagner worked his themes less by development than by repetition and sequence; what had not been realized was how rigorously this work proceeded—"mechanistically" indeed. Furthermore, very curious long-range structures came to light. To take an example from *Die Meistersinger:* the overture is built around four keys (C, E, E flat, and C again) ; then four hours later, and at ten times the length, the final scene of the opera is built around exactly the same keys. Another example, from *Tristan:* the piece begins in A minor and ends in B; the key directly between them, E, is somehow avoided in all the hundreds of modulations contained in the opera—avoided and saved for one appearance: the beautiful passage in Act III where Tristan attains his maximum serene consciousness (*"Wie sie selig, hehr und milde wandelt . . ."*). An example from *Parsifal:* to conclude the piece on a note of huge serenity, Wagner selected the sound of a plagal cadence, already at hand in his "Grail" motive, the so-called Dresden Amen. After moving from the Neapolitan key of D plagally up a fifth to A, he moves up another fifth to E, up another, and another, and another, and another—six times in all, exactly half way around the full tonal circle.

This type of organization is far from twelve-tone organization; but the two have in common a mood, a quality, and that is their schematic quality. An artist who would go so far toward systematization as to multiply a progression six times, might go the rest of the way and group all twelve notes of the scale in a set pattern. An artist so hypersensitive to the key of E major in the five-hour flux of *Tristan und Isolde*, might develop similar concern for the very note *e*, and once he had sounded it, might not want it again until all the eleven other notes had intervened. The parallelism of keys in *Die Meistersinger* brings up a crucial question at once: Has this structure any aesthetic import or is it purely speculative? Is it *heard* or is it an instance of "paper" organization? Something similar is asked about *Ulysses* and the Pound *Cantos*. The very same question is asked all the time about serial music, not only in reference to its formation around the row on a small scale, but also to its modes of coherence on a larger scale. In contemporary criticism this question is central, and the analogy with Wagner should serve as a tool in the answering, or vice versa.

Analogy only; analogy in spirit but not of course in actual detail. With this reservation clear, the link between Wagner and contemporary music may be seen to be more than historical. Wagner's musical organization prefigures in a certain respect Schoenberg's twelve-tone technique and also the fantasy of "total organization" developed by Stockhausen and others. That a technical, even hermetic, aspect of Wagnerism should survive in modern music while more blatant aspects are discredited is, once again, characteristic of the resolute technical limitation of the serialists. The new technical mystique depends even more critically than the Wagnerian on the illusion of organism, on the indestructibility of works that must be judged according to their own "precompositional assumption," on their technical virtuosity, on their logic and economy. And while "economy" is probably the last word that anyone would think of applying to Wagner, it does finally explain itself as the back of the coin of Wagner's insistence on organic synthesis.

Recently, I spent an afternoon looking through the literature on Schoenberg's unfinished opera *Moses und Aron*. Much of this literature is by twelve-tone adherents, and some of it is pretty impressive stuff; yet the name of Wagner is contained in it hardly once. In its fundamental dramatic conception, however, *Moses und Aron* is the most egregiously Wagnerian piece since *Parsifal*. (N.B.—I am not saying that the piece sounds like Wagner, or that Schoenberg's philosophy is as shabby as Wagner's, or that his rhetoric resembles Wagner's; I say simply that in its fundamental dramatic conception, *Moses und Aron* is the most egregiously Wagnerian piece since *Parsifal*.) The work is a didactic racial epic of momentous import. The concept of the *Volk,* indeed the very term, occurs more prominently than ever in Wagner, even in *Die Meistersinger.* The libretto, gauche as only a homemade libretto can be, treats in symbolic terms of universal ethical and political problems; and if Bernard Shaw could see Bakunin and contemporary socialist doctrine in the *Ring,* I can certainly see in *Moses und Aron* the idealistic Zionism of Theodor Herzl and Rabbi Magnes pitted against the political Zionism of Ben-Gurion. The action consists of static dialogues arranged in a stiff dialectic plan—with the exception of the famous Golden Calf Scene, where stage directions out-Wagner Wagner's vanishing castles, swimming Rhine maidens, and magic fires: four Naked Virgins are stabbed and their blood caught in cups, after which rapacious stripping of the chorus is the order of the day. There is blood, sex, *Liebestod,* even the quintessential *Schlange.* There is a direct parallel to, and derivative of, *Stabreim.* There is the by now customary rigorous construction and the enormous complexity of the score. Close to four hundred rehearsals were required for the first performance—shades of *Tristan!*—and that first performance came twenty years after the work was composed, facts which the enthusiasts have greeted with the customary cries of martyrdom and panegyric.

Moses und Aron belongs in this discussion for several reasons. First of all, it bears witness to an almost unbelievable survival of Wagnerian dramatic conception in the work of the central, inescapable, brooding figure of twentieth-century music. Second, it shows how skittishly Wagner is handled today even by the elite (for so the twelve-tone adherents regard themselves). Wagner stands for romanticism; Wagner stands in some obscure way for bogus; his name would taint the modern masterwork. And if this elite shies from Wagner, so much the more does the opera-going public, which sees

Wagner less and less; so much the more does the new, important mass audience made up of phonograph listeners, who
have been able to buy twelve different recordings of *La Bo-
hème* but not a single complete *Siegfried*. This is the age of
Mozart, Webern, perhaps Puccini, maybe Vivaldi, certainly
not Wagner. If courses on the forgotten man are still offered
by certain colleges, that is no doubt a sign of their characteristic archaism.

However, a third reason to bring up *Moses und Aron* is the
serious one. Here is Schoenberg's largest, most ambitious,
and, according to many critics, his greatest work. It is a work
that ought to be in our ears right now, for the posthumous
first performance was only in 1954, the first stage performance came three years later, the record was issued and re-
viewed in 1958, and the third performance recently took
place in Berlin, to the accompaniment of mild riots. *Moses
und Aron* has the authentic aura of a masterpiece. What is
to be made of this piece, with its new problematic dimensions
added to the standard difficulty of any Schoenberg score? The
question, which is scarcely to be met by marching along with
any school or ism, may be helped by Wagner. Wagner is
needed today, if for no other reason than to clarify *Moses
und Aron*. Every element in the latter that calls for clarifica-
tion—the mystique, the complication, the innocence, the impact, the aura—has its analogous element (not identical, but
analogous) in the Wagner canon. It should be as unthinkable
to deny the defects of *Moses* as to deny those of *Parsifal*; it
should be unthinkable to deny the transcendent artistic power
of one work or the other on account of defects. Of course,
nothing will be settled by speculative analogy; what counts
always is the critical ear. But the old work can help define a
stance for the new. The same applies *pari passu* to twelve-

tone music in general, as has been suggested, though there, obviously, the relationship is a good deal more complex.

In short, we have to settle Wagner's debts, and then we have to settle our own debt to Wagner if our credit is to be really good for contemporary music. One might even suppose that close study of Wagner would be necessary for anyone engaging in modern musical composition. However this may be, it is certainly true that a fresh effort to encompass Wagner is necessary for an adequate critical or historical grasp of the music of the present. Answers are needed to the questions about bogus, vulgarity, insincerity, magic, overextension, overcomplication, paper organization, organicism, and the unquestionable incandescence that the operas still attain. This is not the time for such an effort, which I have adumbrated elsewhere. I suggest only one preliminary axiom: resist all pressure to regard the oeuvre as an inviolable, necessary, superbly constructed organic whole. There is no such artistic entity as "Wagner"; only four fantastic works of art —*Tristan, Parsifal,* the *Ring, Die Meistersinger*—with their successful and unsuccessful aspects, with their great beauties and their *bétises.* Organicism is not the issue. Even this much, perhaps, hints at an attitude for more recent music, and indicates the importance of the half-historical, half-critical study that Wagner seems to require, a hundred years after *Tristan.*